The Quality Team Concept in Total Quality Control

The Quality Team Concept in Total Quality Control

John M. Ryan

ASQC Quality Press
Milwaukee, Wisconsin

The Quality Team Concept in Total Quality Control

John M. Ryan

Library of Congress Cataloging-in-Publication Data

Ryan, John M.
    The quality team concept in total quality control/John M. Ryan.
       p.   cm.
    Includes bibliographical references and index.
    ISBN 0-87389-123-6
    1. Total quality management.   2. Just-in-time systems.   I. Title.
HD62.15.R93 1992
658.5'62 — dc20   91-29955
                                                  CIP

10987654321

ISBN 0-87389-123-6

Acquisitions Editor: Jeanine L. Lau
Production Editor: Mary Beth Nilles
Marketing Administrator: Susan Westergard
Set in Janson Text by Zahn-Klicka-Hill. Cover design by Cathy Chojnacki.
Printed and bound by Book Crafters.

For a free copy of the ASQC Quality Press Publications Catalog, including ASQC membership information, call 800-952-6587.

 Printed on Recycled Paper

Printed in the United States of America

ASQC Quality Press
611 East Wisconsin Avenue
Milwaukee, Wisconsin 53202

To Dan and Mark so that they may know a better way, to Robin who always knew one existed, and to Stu Dalke and Abdullah Rafiq who have found the better way many times before.

Contents

Preface

*F*ollowing the Korean War, from the early 1950s through the early 1960s, baby boomers from World War II passed quietly through elementary, junior high, and high school into college. They had been raised in a reasonably idealistic decade. John F. Kennedy's assassination marked the beginning of change.

In rapid succession, Martin Luther King and Robert Kennedy's assassinations, increased environmental awareness, Viet Nam, and the continuing nuclear war threat added fuel to the already collapsing blaze of idealism.

Loss of idealism is a strange thing. If, as one grows older, ideals planted by parents in earlier days are found to be unreal, what is left in the human mind to provide structure for acting out a daily existence? If a person discovers that what one was taught by his/her parents is untrue, what then is true? Suddenly, the structure which guided one in his/her efforts to maintain right from wrong no longer exists.

With the loss of ideals and structure during early adulthood, the individual becomes truly alone. When hundreds of thousands of people suffer this agony together, cultural change is born.

The trauma from this loss of faith in the perceived truth and subsequent loss of guiding structure results in a clash of ideal and real. This can be devastating to entire cultures as well as to individuals.

America reacted to this change with clashes between generations. Older people (over 30) had already come to grips with reality through earlier and harsher lessons. Over time, they had somehow justified things and adjusted, but the 1960s generation could not cope using traditional adjustment techniques. The general reaction to a loss of idealism accompanied by a loss of structure was expressed through a search for alternative life-styles, dress, music, and philosophies. It was a time of change, but the change was almost random.

Slowly but surely, the young began to redevelop a life structure which would guide them through their own growth and development. Some of the things their parents had taught them were found to be sound and worthwhile. These teachings were combined with the bag of beliefs and behaviors each of us carries around. Other ideals and beliefs taught by parents were discarded or replaced with more versatile, or more restricted philosophies. Each person who experienced this discard and restructure exercise also experienced great personal agony and difficulty. Some individuals never completed the task, while others are prospering because of their successful restructure.

A new structure of idealism versus reality was born. It is not the same as that of our parents.

Most of us who were young during the 1960s, the Viet Nam war, assassinations, demonstrations, and burnings ended up over 20 years later with a different perspective of the world.

Today, as the older generation looks at us, the children of the 1960s don't appear so different, but we are. We exist by the millions and hold some of the top jobs in industry, government, education, and health. We have different perspectives and we are not as afraid of change as some of our parents might have been. It is likely that some of the most serious organizational challenges in history are now coming from this generation.

In their search for excellence among American companies, Tom Peters and Robert Watterman, Jr. discovered, indeed, continue to search and discover, something about dynamism.[12, 13] An increasing number of companies have begun to make new adjustments to the world of business. Just as the youth of the 1960s lost their beliefs to harsh realities, business has had to begin the difficult, gut-wrenching task of self examination. They must do this to eliminate philosophies and practices that no longer work, and to replace them with something new.

American business is in the process of restructuring. Those companies unable to restructure, redefine, and recoup will not survive in world competition. Those firms that successfully redefine reality and develop a structure supportive of that belief system will survive and succeed. The key to successful restructuring lies with the people in the organization and the teamwork they are able to develop and sustain.

Tom Peters writes about redefining reality. This book presents a team structure developed to support that reality.

Introduction

This book's intent is to provide the reader with a comprehensive look at how various techniques, methods, and strategies fit together to restructure an organization's culture by building and implementing an overall team approach to total quality control/just-in-time (TQC/JIT). Additionally, this text illustrates how a company can work step-by-step through the processes of training, teamwork, and management change to reach a position where the system is self-perpetuating and improvement is continuous. The emphasis is on cost savings through system implementation.

Examples from TQC/JIT companies in the United States, Korea, Mexico, and Thailand are included throughout the book.

Most companies already have implemented or attempted to implement some of the techniques discussed herein. This is an advantage because such efforts are cumulative and leave less to be done in the future. Employees probably already have some concepts and ideas with which to work. As W. Edwards Deming has stated, "If you don't know where to start, start somewhere."

The book is not intended to motivate managers to seek process improvement. If you are reading this book, you already have recognized a need in your company which requires corrective action. Whether that corrective action was inspired by financial losses, customer returns, excessive inventory, or costly processes, the need has been felt. It is hoped that the motivational factors are established within you.

Generally, the person or management team most likely to successfully achieve true process control is the person already most motivated. Such a person will become the effort's true leader. True leaders always have been successful.

Included are many examples and case histories which are not manufacturing related. This is in line with true TQC/JIT philosophies. Any company which chooses to focus only on manufacturing is, in effect, saying that manufacturing is the cause of their financial woes, scrap, poor yields, excessive inventories, and, eventually, lost business. Nothing could be farther from the truth. It has been our experience to find that manufacturing is like the tail of a whip. If designs are poor, tooling unable to hold process capabilities, drawings inaccurate or out of revision, data entered late or inaccurately into a computer, or if customer response time is slow, manufacturing will suffer. These are only a few of the indications of a poorly managed company. All of these problems contribute to manufacturing problems. All of these problems are expensive and are solvable using the system outlined herein.

The bottom line is that any TQC/JIT effort requires people support. The system is people based and demands a high level of involvement. Many managers have grasped at statistical process control (SPC) or other miracle solutions to poor yields. In truth, SPC or any other systematic approach to process improvement is miraculous only to the extent that people learn how to use the tools and are organized and supported as required. Although SPC is not dealt with in-depth herein, SPC should be clearly understood to be of critical necessity to team problem solving efforts.

During the course of implementing TQC/JIT system components, management will be faced with the attitude of "It won't work" or "We can't." There is simply no place for such attitudes in today's business world. Doing things right the first time must become the standard of every company, regardless of the service or product sold. If management cannot agree on and communicate a clear-cut dedication to continuous quality and time standard improvements, the battle will be lost before it has begun. Every single employee must understand and be dedicated to obtaining increasing shares of future business by building a reputation second to none.

Any company with quality or in-time process problems must honestly answer the question, "How much time each week do we allow our employees to identify and solve problems?" Most companies provide little forum for group problem solving outside of day-to-day fire fight scrambling. To never turn the corner into a preventive mode means that problems are not being solved at all, but are merely being bandaged.

This text includes six chapters. Chapter 1 discusses the basic TQC/JIT system and many of the attitudes and ideas that make the system work.

Chapter 2 carefully outlines the development of an organization designed to establish, implement, and sustain the overall corporate cultural change required for success. Managerial responsibilities are separated from nonmanagerial responsibilities, and team formation and functioning are covered.

Chapter 3 focuses on a recommended series of specific steps various teams should follow as they attempt to implement the TQC/JIT system.

Chapter 4 expands team concepts into specialized manufacturing teams required to support the TQC/JIT efforts as floor space is redesigned, and new methods of thinking take place to support the in-depth corporate culture change.

Chapter 5 focuses primarily on costs, ways to think about costs, and ways to analyze and prioritize costs which then become targets of preventive action.

Chapter 6 summarizes the system's main steps and its implementation.

The appendices include forms and models developed in companies from such areas as southern California, Mexico, Korea, and Southeast Asia (Thailand).

1

Basic
TQC/JIT
Concepts

This book is intended to guide the reader through the twists and turns of implementation. Although many specific tools are discussed, references are provided to guide the reader to a greater understanding of some of these tools.

The emphasis of TQC/JIT is to reduce wasted time and material in an effort to save money. Saved money means profitability. Costs must be measured and attacked.

There are always some misunderstandings regarding TQC and JIT. To set the stage for clearer understanding, the concept presented is that total quality control (TQC) is the overall system within which just-in-time (JIT) operates. JIT is perceived as one of many tools that operate under a TQC umbrella. Other tools include statistical process control, cause-and-effect analysis, audits and surveys, experimentation, design reviews, data collection and analysis, and many more.

With increasing international competition, JIT concepts and practices have been shown to be critical to supplementing an organization's profitability. While JIT practices are in many ways different from what most quality practitioners currently perceive to be of importance, such concepts and practices enhance the overall team approach to solving a multitude of problems which are not usually thought of as "quality" problems.

Total quality control means just that. Every division, section, and person must be involved continually in the quality effort. Error rates in all parts of the company must be reduced. First-time, error-free work is critical; mistakes are costly. There are simply no exceptions to this rule. Figure 1.1 illustrates this thinking. Each main function shown on Figure 1.1 is, in many organizations, a separate department, often headed by a different manager. Only limited experience in an organization will teach a newcomer that the statement, "That's a quality problem!" may be interpreted to mean "It's not my job!" to solve quality problems. It should be clearly understood that every department contributes to the creation of quality problems, and that every department must organize to reduce the likelihood and occurrence of problems emanating from their group. The responsibility for the organization's quality reputation clearly rests with management and management's ability to develop and maintain teamwork within and across departmental barriers. The ultimate product or process quality, whether in a manufacturing or a service industry environment depends on every person in the organization.

Management teamwork must exist in order for this level of organizational penetration to work. Chapter 2 explains how to develop management teamwork supportive of the activities of non-managerial personnel. Figure 1.1 attempts to show how different functions can cause quality problems, implying that managers must commit to collectively attack problems. Table 1.1 is a more specific list of how different people from departments responsible for manufacturing support might work together on teams focusing on various problem areas. For example, the table shows that vendor relationships should be worked on by team members from production (PROD), engineering (ENG), quality (QUAL), purchasing (PUR), and production control (PC). These teams, combined with the

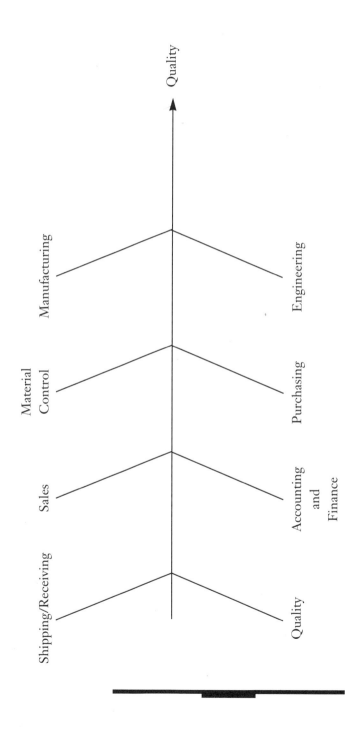

Figure 1.1 Management Teamwork
Objective: Reduce Quality Costs

Table 1.1   Specialized Teams: Manufacturing Focused

Team Focus	Recommended Members
Pilot Line	PROD/ENG/QUAL/PC
Vendor Relationships	PROD/ENG/QUAL/PUR/PC
Value Engineering	PROD/ENG/QUAL/PUR/DES
Design for Manufacturability	PROD/ENG/QUAL/DES
Parts Commonality	ENG/DES
Preventive Maintenance	PROD/MAINT
Foolproofing (Poka-Yoke)	PROD/QUAL/ENG/DES
Process Layout and Line Balance	PROD/ENG
Lot Size Reduction	PROD/PC
Organize and Clean Workplace	PROD/ENG
KANBAN	PROD/PC/PUR
Line Stop	PROD/QUAL
Statistical Process Control	PROD/QUAL
Visual Signals (ANDON)	PROD/QUAL
Training (Certification)	PROD
Setup Time Reduction	PROD/ENG
Automation Review	PROD/ENG
Cycle Time Control	PROD/ENG

importance of design (DES) are discussed in more detail in Chapter 4. Such specialized teams form the backbone of JIT implementation.

This thinking implies that JIT strategies and tools are a subset of TQC. The overriding objective of the system is to improve quality. Without quality improvement, there can be no true JIT, but there can be TQC without using JIT tools. While TQC focuses on errors, JIT tends to focus more on factors related to time, space,

**Table 1.2   Comparative Elements
TQC/JIT**

	TQC	JIT
Organizational Elements		
Top-Level Commitment and Involvement	X	X
Planned	X	X
100% Employee Involvement	X	X
Delegation of Authority and Responsibility	X	X
Corrective Action Teams	X	X
Functional Quality Improvement Groups	X	X
Identify and Commit to Internal Customers	X	X
Cycle of Improvement	X	X
Cost Focus	X	X
Results and Recognition Orientation	X	X

and inventory. Imagine what a company with no errors could accomplish if time factors were minimized, space conserved, and inventory managed in a manner that allowed for high annual inventory turns. These ideas will be explored later.

> *Error-free, fast-flowing products and services is the overall goal.*

The same type of thinking holds true for other common quality subsystems as well. Statistical process control (SPC), quality control circles (QCC), quality cost analyses, and many other subsystems and tools are perceived as useful, even essential, to a TQC effort.

Surprisingly, the confusion between TQC and JIT comes from the elements and directions they share in common. Table 1.2 lists some common but important basic shared comparative elements.

Top-level commitment and involvement are absolutely necessary.[10] This means that the top management in an organization must be committed to quality and that they must spend time and lead the way to implementing the changes required for implementation and maintenance of a TQC/JIT system. The top-level team (TLT) generally meets in a specific time and place each week to dedicate their time and effort to the problems associated with system planning and management.

No TQC or JIT system was ever implemented without serious planning. Both perspectives generally represent monumental organizational changes to the current way of doing things within an organization and both are to be perceived as threats to persons with certain personality and managerial styles. Luckily, we find that those threatened by such change are easily identified through their comments and actions. Identification of problems is the first step toward their solutions. In order to overcome an obstacle such as reluctant personnel, involvement in the early stages of system planning generally allows input and establishes ownership, thus reducing resistance.

Again, no employee or department is sacred or free from the likelihood that something takes too long, or that errors are made. One hundred percent employee involvement is critical (unless employees already are doing everything perfectly).

The importance of companywide involvement presents a serious challenge. Anthropological studies of cultural change have indicated that the most significant self-sustaining changes occur when the change is accepted by those it is intended to change.[7] Furthermore, attempts to force change or to make involvement mandatory leads to conformance, but not to true acceptance of ideas and actions.[1] This presents a conflict for systematic change efforts which stress the need for total involvement.

One hundred percent involvement is a goal which can be reached in many different ways. Some companies have approached this conflict by making involvement mandatory. Mandatory involvement, however, has been repeatedly shown to be a weak and short-term change agent and should be discarded as an idea for TQC/JIT system implementation. The required managerial emphasis should be on rewarding those emerging TQC/JIT stars with promotions and raises while leaving nonsupporters without recognition or reward.

With any employee-based continuous improvement effort (which includes almost all quality improvement work), managers must learn to delegate authority and responsibility to lower levels. Many managers have problems allowing lower-level personnel to make decisions.[3] They have problems surrendering their power and authority. The problems associated with this type of manager, and some possible solutions, are discussed more fully in Chapter 2. Top-level managers must become leaders in this effort to force lower-level decision making. Often this includes a top-level manager abdicating a leadership slot in a group, thus allowing another team member to practice group leadership skills. This approach simultaneously aids the company in its quest to internally develop the strong leaders required for continued business growth and success.

In addition to the top-level team responsible for planning and managing the TQC/JIT effort, interdepartmental corrective action teams (CATs) and functional improvement teams (FITs) are the next two types of groups formed to support the system. The interdepartmental corrective action team's purpose is to identify and solve problems that cross boundaries between departments. An example is a CAT with members from facilities, engineering, production, quality, and administration who are responsible for solving a problem of excess contamination in a plant.

Functional improvement teams include members only from the functional group in question. Usually this includes a manager and his/her direct reports. For example, a product engineering group may attack the problem of excess errors in drawings caused by members of that group.

There is another critical similarity between TQC and JIT systems which must be highlighted here. The concept of the "customer" in most companies continues to be that of some nebulous company somewhere which receives either services or products or both. This type of thinking is detrimental to TQC and JIT functioning. Every individual in a TQC/JIT functioning company must think of the specific product or service they are personally responsible for delivering to the next person. That next person is known as the internal customer. The principles we all have learned which motivate companies to serve external customers must also apply to the person or department down the hall or around the corner from our own workplace. The goal of every individual must be to produce first-time error-free work in time for the next person to accurately and quickly accomplish his/her own job. The next person cannot adequately perform the job while having to correct our errors, ask for us to correct it, or rush through a job which was delivered late.

Improvement must be perceived as a never-ending cycle. Under the principles of TQC and JIT, good is never good enough until perfection is reached. Perfection does not mean that every part or service must be perfectly centered on the nominal dimension, although that is the goal. Perfection simply means that every part or service must meet the requirements of the next person, department, or specification. Reaching this level of perfection requires a group consciousness focused on continuous improvement in ever-tightening cycles. Patience on management's part is critical because this process can, and often does, take years.

There is no sense to a system that costs more than it can save a company. As often as possible, improvements made to manufacturing or service processes should be cost justified. This means that some manner of measuring success is required. The results of the continuous improvement effort should be measured and reported in terms of money. A trend line of costs, whether due to rework, scrap, returns, or lost time, should be plotted with the group's goal set at reducing these costs. Often this is difficult, but it can be simplified so that the group can focus clearly on the problem, its causes, and solutions. (Chapter 5 focuses on simple, systematic techniques for collecting and analyzing cost data.)

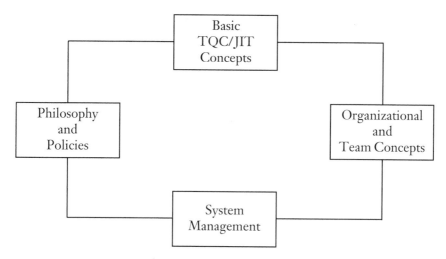

Figure 1.2 TQC/JIT

Since both TQC and JIT are so highly people dependent, both require that positive results be recognized and rewarded. This reward structure helps to ensure that motivational levels are maintained. Management must ask itself why people should continue to be motivated if all rewards go to management when it is the large number of nonmanagerial personnel upon whom success depends. This does not imply that managers are not important. Certainly, managerial errors cost companies more than operator errors.

ACTION OUTLINE

When it comes to TQC/JIT system implementation, there are four main areas with which management must be concerned (Figure 1.2). (1) The top-level management team must understand, support, and ensure that all employees have knowledge of basic TQC/JIT concepts. (2) After initial management training, management has the responsibility to develop a supporting organization consisting of several levels of managerial and corrective action teams.

(3) Management must also develop, commit to, and actively lead employees in the planning and implementation of TQC/JIT philosophies and policies. (4) Finally, managers must work continuously to manage the TQC/JIT system. Perhaps the greatest problem with implementation of TQC systems is that managers frequently are found to resist assuming new managerial responsibilities required for successful implementation. (The many ways resistance may occur are discussed in Chapter 2.)

If these major managerial tasks are accomplished, implementation will occur throughout all organizational levels with increasing consistency. Managers will be free to manage and employees will be free to improve all operations. In Table 1.3, managers are responsible for steps one through four. All other employees are responsible for steps 4A through 4M (see Chapter 3).

It should be clear at this point that management is expected to manage the system. This is a large task. All employees must receive TQC/JIT training if they are expected to perform as management desires. With training, the employees will become the implementers while the top-level team managers remain managers, free to manage.

Decisions must be made close to the point of action. Team members must make decisions to attempt change for purposes of improvement. Management should not make all of these decisions. The best way to ensure that good decisions are made at lower levels is to train all employees so that the decisions made outside of the manager's control are consistent with those the manager would have made as continuous improvement and cost reductions are sought.

Table 1.3 represents the basic steps required to implement a TQC/JIT system. Steps one through four have been briefly discussed. These steps will be explored throughout this text. Each step appears reasonably simple to accomplish, however, the steps required to organize and implement the system are complex and require dedicated management. (These steps are discussed in detail in Chapters 2 and 3. Table 2.1 and Figure 3.1 expand on these concepts and include specific implementation information.)

Table 1.3   Implementation Steps: System Management

1. Train top management in basic TQC/JIT concepts.

2. Develop an organizational approach: Form a top-level team.

3. Establish the guiding philosophy and communicate the change to all employees.

4. Plan, implement, and manage the system using the following sequence of steps:

    A. Each department or group should choose one process or problem to attack.

    B. Choose team members and a team leader. Corrective action teams (CATs) and functional improvement teams (FITs) are established and operated according to guidelines (e.g., Table 1.1).

    C. Develop the team's primary goal. Focus on costs.

    D. Flowchart the process to be improved.

    E. Develop methods to establish baseline measurements and reporting. This data must be *plotted* to show cost, defect, and cycle time trends.

    F. Collect data to establish the baseline. Do *not* change the measurement or analytical methods throughout corrective action attempts.

    G. Measure average costs, cycle times, hours per unit, or defect levels for each step in the process chosen for improvement. Plot the data.

    H. Compare and list the costs, cycle times, defect levels, or hours per unit using the process flowchart.

    I. Analyze the data using the process flowchart and choose the specific step most likely to show the greatest improvement if corrective action is successful. Using cycle times and hours per unit, this usually is the process step that takes

(Table 1.3 continued)

the greatest amount of time. If defect data are used, a Pareto chart will not indicate the defect causing the highest level cost or reject losses. Cost data must always be analyzed.

J. Write a corrective action plan showing corrective action objectives, time lines, and the person responsible for the completion of each objective.

K. Implement the plan and monitor and report results using the format developed in steps E, F, and G.

L. Compare the corrective action results to the baseline data and the goal.

M. Repeat steps G through L until the cycle time or defect level is reduced to a satisfactory level. This step represents the concept of continuous improvement.

Table 1.3 does not include the numerous tools and concepts required to accomplish each step. (These are described below.) Table 1.3 reveals the basic ongoing approaches used to achieve TQC and JIT improvements.

DEFINITIONS

Before beginning discussion of the implementation steps, some definitions are provided to guide the reader's understanding of terms used throughout the book. Table 1.4 summarizes these terms.

Table 1.4 Terms Defined

Quality – Meeting the requirements the first time at the source (where the product or service originates).

(Table 1.4 continued)

Pull System: KANBAN – A system of authorizing each person in the process to build only when the next operation has pulled product or paper out of the KANBAN.

Internal Customer – The person receiving the output of the previous step in a process.

External Customer – The company or person receiving a company's output.

Nonvalue-Adding Activities – Any activity that does not add directly to the ideal cost of a product or service.

Ideal Cost – The sales value of a product or service which will enable the company to compete on a worldwide basis.

Quality

The idea that quality means "meeting the requirements" is not complex. If requirements do not exist, quality cannot be measured. The message that every job must be done correctly the first time, every time is critical. On a manufacturing line, specifications and work standards are usually established to guide the product's quality.

The same concept should hold true in engineering. If new engineers do not know how drawing packages are completed or routed correctly because requirements are not clear or are incomplete, it is impossible for them to produce quality drawing packages that meet the needs of internal customers. If cleanliness requirements are not clearly established for a facility, how can facility personnel be blamed for the lack of cleanliness?

Another good example of a lack of requirements often is found in a purchasing department where purchase orders require buyers to contact the people who filled out the purchase order because the order is incomplete or unclear. The result is that the buyer must do rework, waste time, and often orders the wrong item. Usually this situation occurs due to either a lack of written requirements or a lack of training. These are management problems which can and are solved through TQC/JIT system strategies.

KANBAN

The pull system concept (KANBAN) is particular to JIT, but serves to help control inventory and exposure to catastrophic quality problems. Theoretically, a person can, with quality and safety, accomplish a single technical task at one time. Some people are more adept at juggling many tasks, but they only address one at a time. If a process, whether paperwork or product, is balanced or without bottlenecks, the work may be pulled through the process rather than pushed. The result is that the work flow remains smoother, more controllable, faster, and more easily corrected than if a huge pile of rework has been built up.

Customers

Internal and external customers differ greatly in their needs. Generally, most companies, departments, or sections do not consider the receiver of their work to be a customer. Rather, the next person or department in line is considered a nuisance because they often complain that what they received is not correct. Sometimes they do not complain, but simply add to the already incorrect work by adding their own version of what they should be doing. The end result is compounded errors, thus slower accomplishment of the job because of the high level of rework required.

The practice of providing internal customers with quality as-built products and services is an act resulting from attitudes that are absolutely critical in order to satisfy external customer demands. Such attitudes and acts must become accepted daily practices within all parts of the company.

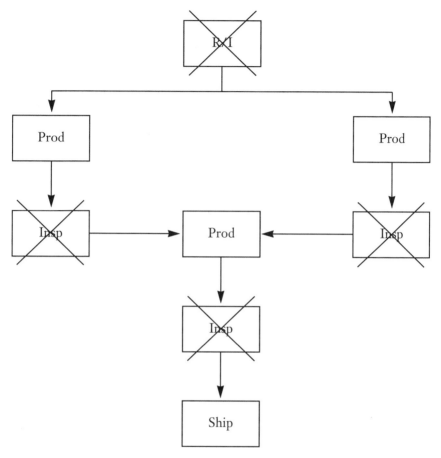

Figure 1.3   Nonvalue-Adding Operations

Nonvalue-Adding Activities

Nonvalue-adding activities are simple to identify. No inspection or rework operation adds value.[21] They should be targets for cost savings elimination (Figure 1.3). Similarly, time spent by the purchasing department cleaning up purchase orders is rework time. Some companies have a *touch-up* operation after flow solder. Touch-up is another word for rework. Rework time does not add value to products or services.

Ideal Costs

Costs are of prime concern to all companies. Chapter 5 gives some guidance to collecting and analyzing costs associated with defect levels and long throughput times. Regardless of the cost analysis methods used, the primary focus of a team's activities should be to save the company money. This means that it is not always possible for teams to depend on sound accounting principles, practices, and people to arrive at costs. Standard burdened costs will help teams to estimate the extent of not only the problem, but the effects of corrective action.

Ideal costs should become targets for all companies. The world is no longer a small place. In today's market, the ideal factory is said to be on roller skates. This means the factory should be able to relocate with the least amount of effort in the least amount of time.[17] This is done because the sales price of many products is constantly lowering. In order to compete on a worldwide basis, companies must compete with the lowest priced producer in the world, not just with the lowest priced local producer. Companies able to achieve ideal costs with good quality are said to be *world class* companies able to compete anywhere in the world.

Conversely, companies that successfully reduce their costs through TQC and JIT strategies have no need to move.

CONCEPTS SPECIFIC TO JIT

As previously stated, TQC and JIT share many basic and important ideas and concepts. However, at first glance, some concepts that are JIT concepts do not appear to be related to TQC. Table 1.5 summarizes some critical JIT ideas which must be clearly understood since they form the basis of time reduction efforts. Successful implementation of the JIT part of the TQC/JIT effort requires that every employee think in terms of the following:

Table 1.5   Basic JIT Concepts

- Visualize what your process would look like if parts were converted to finished goods with as *few* steps as possible. The same vision is required for all processes, whether they are designed to build parts, serve hamburgers, or process engineering documentation.
- View inventory and paperwork as moving, not as static.
- Concentrate on synchronization of each process. All parts of the process should be producing to the same heartbeat.
- The three principles of JIT are:
  - Simplify
  - Combine
  - Eliminate
- The wastes are:
  - Overproduction
  - Unnecessary production steps
  - Transportation, handling
  - Excessive inventory
  - Excessive motion
  - Waiting (underproduction)

Discussion of Table 1.5 is important.

Nearly all processes contain some unnecessary steps. If JIT-conscious employees are involved, they sometimes need to go into a quiet room to think about the flow of products or services. If they can use their minds to *see* the flow, they also can see the flow with fewer steps. Employees must visualize motion reduction, wait-time reduction, operation recombination, production lines being moved closer to the next line (thereby eliminating handling between lines), the removal of unnecessary inspection, and other TQC/JIT concepts.

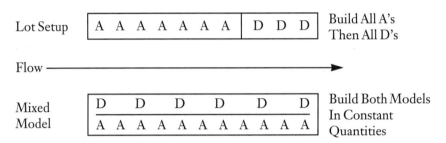

Figure 1.4 Production Mix

In one case, two operators were observed sitting next to each other. The first operator performed an alignment and swaging operation while the next one inspected the product and, if rejected, deswaged and returned it to the swaging station. The reject (and rework) rate was 20%. The line had been running like this since it was first set up eight months earlier. The swaging fixture could not hold tolerance. The way to eliminate this built-in inspection and rework operation was to redesign the fixture and add a reticle to the first operator's microscope eyepiece. The problem was solved, rejects disappeared, and an inspection station was eliminated.

Everyone has seen movies of factories which are fully automated. Parts are constantly moving through different machines which act on them in different ways. This continuously moving river of parts being acted on one piece at a time is an ideal outcome of a successful JIT conversion. In truth, however, most operations where JIT ideas are applied are labor intensive. JIT takes over where the machines leave off. JIT is people-dependent and people-oriented.

Operators who may have worked on the same job for years now have the opportunity to learn new skills and jobs. This occurs because in a balanced JIT line parts are moving smoothly, but operations occasionally get out of balance and one operator must help another. In other cases, the position of an ill employee can be supported by operators on either side if both are cross-trained. For the operators, successfully completing cross-training means higher pay and eventual promotion. Most importantly, operators with knowledge critical to the improvement of the process now have the opportunity to collectively use their minds to solve problems. These people become increasingly flexible, creative, and responsible for the success of their operations. The spin-off effect is newfound job enjoyment.

The concept of synchronization concerns how well process steps are balanced to support each other. In an office, one secretary may adequately cover the demands of five engineers. If not, a bottleneck will occur in which the secretary cannot get the work out as fast or as accurately as requirements demand. The same holds true for manufacturing lines. By breaking up massive blocks of identical production into smaller, more versatile piece part to final product lines, teams are formed, cross-training can take place, problems can be solved as they occur, and simplification, elimination, and combination of tasks becomes more visible and manageable.

The change in production mix in Figure 1.4 illustrates this difference. In the "Lot Set up" model, part numbers change as they flow through the entire factory. In the "Mixed Model" two different manufacturing JIT lines handle two different volume requirements for two different products over different rates of production. The line balance, layout, space, personnel, and equipment requirements are different. Operators do not have to change from one specification to another, thereby allowing for quality improvements without sacrificing volume requirements. The line flow simply is more visible to all observers; including operators, production leads and managers, quality personnel, and engineers.

Figure 1.5 shows a standard way to collect production data from the factory floor. Performance analysis is measured in scheduled units against actual performance and is summarized as production per hour. Figure 1.6 shows the type of data to be collected in a JIT line. Critical trend indices that are collected at the end of day include completed assemblies, ending inventory, hours per unit, rework, scrap, and cycle time data. These are plotted and used to manage the line.

Figures 1.7 through 1.11 show trend lines for an actual Korean manufacturing JIT line during its first two months of effort. All lines trend in positive directions and tend to demonstrate increasing stability in the manufacturing process. The circled point on Figure 1.7 shows a product change in the JIT line. Notice how quickly the line recovered and continued its trend toward improvement. The "Ending Inventory" (Figure 1.8) shows a marked improvement in decreased inventory near the end of the measurement period. The

Time	Scheduled Units	Accumulated Units	Production This Hour	Remarks
8 – 9 AM	100	98	98	Material Short
9 – 10 AM	100	190	109	
10 – 11 AM	100	278	80	Oven Failure
11 – 12 AM	100	378	100	

Figure 1.5   Performance Analysis

JIT Line _____

Date	Completed Assemblies	Ending Inventory	HPU	Units Rework	Units Scrap	Cycle Time	Remarks

Figure 1.6   Performance Analysis

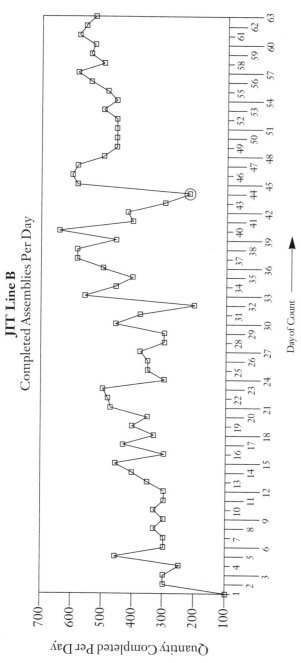

JIT Line B
Completed Assemblies Per Day

Quantity Completed Per Day

Day of Count

Figure 1.7

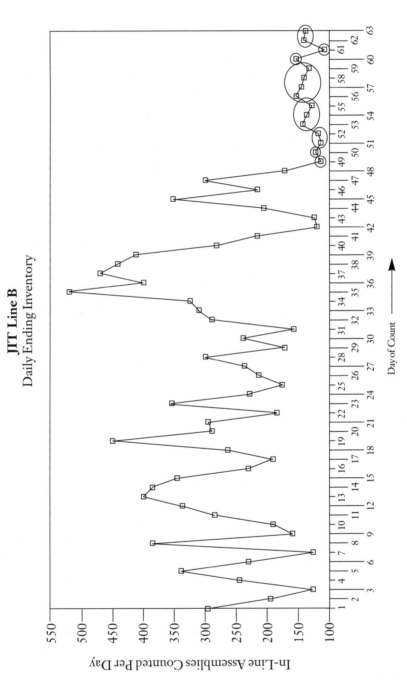

Figure 1.8

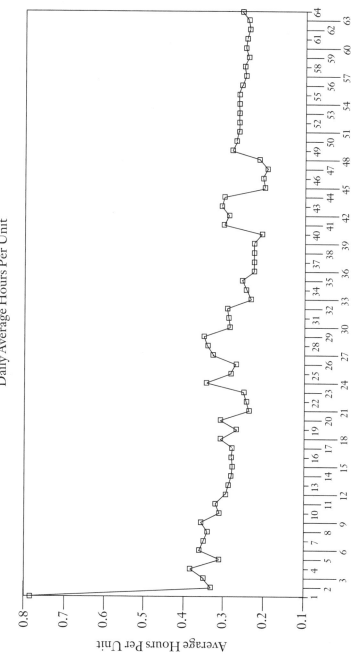

JIT Line B
Daily Average Hours Per Unit

Figure 1.9

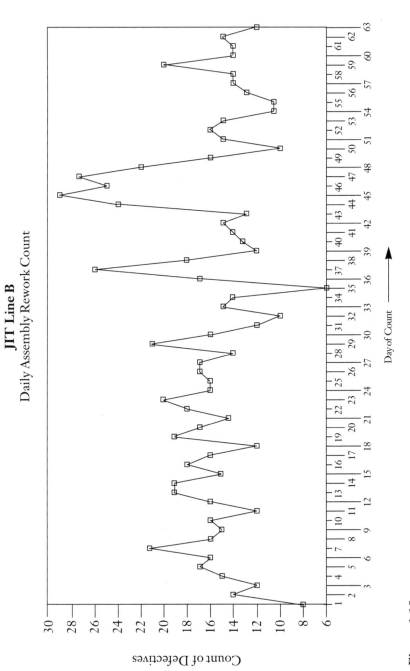

Figure 1.10

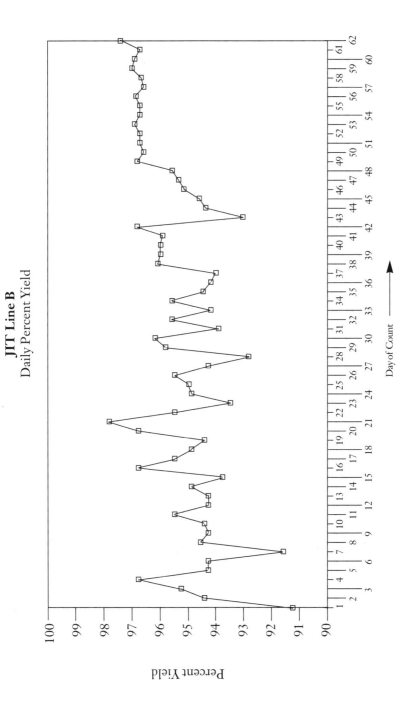

JIT Line B
Daily Percent Yield

Figure 1.11

circled points indicate that this was the period when a true KANBAN was established and the line went into a pull system.

It should be noted that the effort represented by trend lines in Figures 1.7 through 1.11 was set up with experienced operators. The trend lines represent improvement over what had been achieved in a traditional line, and do not represent learning curve achievement.

PREVENTION

Discussions about TQC/JIT implementation are not complete without consideration of the critical concept of prevention. Preventive actions are money savers! Chapter 5 focuses on team and system approaches for identifying and measuring costs of doing things wrong. Such costs can be prevented. The emphasis is on preventing wasteful costs from recurring.

Unfortunately, the word "prevention" is often thrown around as though everyone should have a good grasp of its meaning. Often, prevention is discussed in quality cost terms (Figure 1.12). The theory is that the more a company spends on prevention, the less it must spend on inspection, test, rework, scrap, etc. The paybacks for such preventive efforts as training, design to manufacture, etc., have proven to be substantial by many companies. Somehow, however, a truer meaning of prevention continues to escape most people.

In a manner similar to what happens when a manager demands *reduced costs* or *customer service* without operationalizing the terms, interpretations and the actions which follow often create havoc in a company.[2, 6] As an example, *customer service* means different things to different departments. Everyone seems to agree that improved customer service is an honorable, indeed, critical goal. However, when the sales department *services* a customer by ramming pull-ins and push-outs through engineering, scheduling, production control, and manufacturing, the end result is delayed service and product. Thus, the end result is poorer customer service.

The rationalization that customer schedule changes must take

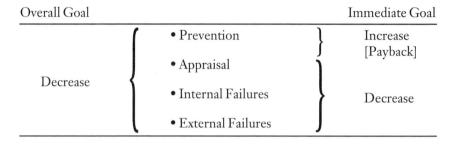

Figure 1.12   *Quality Costs*

priority because a company dedicates itself to "customer service" more than likely means the salesperson wants to be a hero in the eyes of the customer. Indeed, telling a favored customer that a schedule pull-in is impossible is not something a salesperson wants to do. It might be easier to exert one's power by waving the banner of customer service than to carefully ensure that other customer schedules are not interrupted. After all, the other customers may be someone else's customers.

Preventive vs. Corrective Action

Webster's New World Dictionary defines prevent as "3. to keep from happening; make impossible by prior action; hinder."[24] This definition does not imply that fire fighting is preventive! Indeed, corrective action, if done without consideration for prevention, certainly is not preventive and not truly corrective. Corrective action haphazardly performed without a deliberate intent to prevent a recurrence is irresponsible. To prevent defects means that their occurrence is "made impossible by prior action."

The concept of prevention appears difficult for most people to understand, therefore it is difficult to implement. If we were to walk into any factory, pick up a control chart showing an out-of-control condition, go to the process and begin searching for the problem, we would be in the beginning stages of corrective action. Ninety-nine times out of 100 the problem will be corrected only to recur at a later date.

For example, a Korean operator noticed that wire was not tinning properly. She notified her lead who summoned an engineer. The solder pot temperature was checked and found to be correct. Other tinning operators were having no problems indicating that one product line was affected. In a short period, the quality of the wire insulation was determined to be the culprit. All wire from the original roll was purged from the line, along with all product built from that roll (over 5,000 defective units). The offending roll of wire was removed from the storeroom and returned to the vendor.

Is that the end of the story? Not if prevention is considered. True, corrective action had taken place and everyone concerned could, with reasonably clear conscience, say they had done a good job and returned to their desks. Unfortunately, the storeroom held two more defective rolls of wire, waiting to go onto the line. A quick test of all wire was set up, the two defective rolls found and removed. A permanent receiving inspection specification was written, implemented at the factory and faxed back to the vendor. Not until the wire vendor's vendor had found and fixed the cause was the problem considered prevented.

Numerous questions arose from this situation. Why wouldn't the wire tin? Why did it get into the manufacturing line? Why wasn't a specification written? Why did it come from the vendor? Why was it caused at the vendor's vendor? The team could not rest or drop the issue until the problem's true cause was found and prevented. What was the cost of reworking (plus inspection and scrap) the 5,000 pieces already built?

All problems, whether manufacturing or administrative, must be relentlessly pursued until preventive attitudes and practices are put into practice. How is this done?

Preventive Methods

Planning. A preventive company takes planning seriously. The plans to upgrade or implement a preventive TQC/JIT system should reflect the company's intentions three to five years in advance. Putting a good preventive system in place takes a great deal of time, money, and effort and cannot be done in a piecemeal, fad, reactive manner. Furthermore, the cooperative interdepartmental development, approval, and implementation of the plan is essential to achieving a homogeneously executed companywide prevention system.

Policy. Does the company's written quality policy specifically state that the company emphasizes prevention as a strategic method of daily operation? Is prevention defined? Have the major powers in the company signed the policy to strongly indicate that this is their policy and that they are willing to back it up with the organization, planning, etc., to make it work? If not, this is a good place to start.

Management teamwork. The TLT, FITs, and CATs meet weekly to review problems and to assume responsibilities for quality issues. Data are reviewed, priorities set, and, most importantly, the attitude of "It's not my problem" is actively attacked. These meetings also serve to address problems in a constructive manner, as opposed to one that is destructive, defensive, and finger-pointing. When an issue gets hot, the approach is to collectively determine a strategy that will solve the problem through systematic efforts rather than to place blame (thereby covering one's own behind). Management must be involved, responsible, responsive, and committed to the quality of products and services delivered by the company.

Design to manufacture. Some of the most costly manufacturing failures result from a lack of focus by designers who fail to understand manufacturing requirements. Design reviews are critical at preproduction stages. The company that rushes sales orders through, in order to meet overly optimistic delivery dates, leaving no time for thorough multidepartmental design review, is going to lose more money than the company that takes design and design review seriously. The two days of response time saved by ignoring design needs usually end up costing weeks at some later date.

Each company's design and review system must be appraised in light of rework rates and customer returns related to design failures. Compilation of financial losses sometimes help management to understand the magnitude of the problem.

Training. Let's face it, on-the-job (OJT) training usually means that a company throws inexperienced operators on the line because new orders have caused a rapid ramp up. Nothing can be more disastrous for quality and throughput speed. Often, a company will emphasize OJT because formal training costs money (prevention money) and managers are not convinced that such money is well spent. Usually this is true because many of today's managers came up through the ranks and never had formal training themselves. Unplanned or nonexistent training are guaranteed ways to cause defectives and lose money. Prevention means stopping losses. The company with no formal planned training program for all levels is not operating in a preventive mode.

Operators certainly need experience and certification in their specific operation. They also need cross-certification in a JIT environment. In addition to company orientation, most personnel should know basic TQC/JIT concepts, teamwork responsibilities (including the various tools presented in Chapter 3), what the product they are building does and is used for, quality specifications, workmanship standards, and some statistical process control techniques.[4] Similarly, engineers, production control personnel, leads, supervisors, and managerial personnel need similar training in addition to managerial training.

Training should be viewed as an ongoing upgrading of expertise for all personnel. A professionally planned and managed curriculum should be developed and implemented over time. No company can expect to competently train all employees in a short time period. However, the time it takes to train personnel in TQC/JIT should be planned with the company's survivability in mind. A company

Table 1.6 Training Items

Course A:	Basic TQC/JIT concepts
	Quality philosophy
	Organization
	Implementation
Course B:	Team concepts – leadership/membership
Course C:	Check sheets
	Histograms
	Ishikawa diagrams
	Cycle time analysis
Course D:	Corrective action
	• Setting corrective action goals
	• Action plan

Group 1:	Management, engineers, supervisors, technicians
Group 2:	Leads, operators
Group 3:	Leads, operators
Group 4:	Leads, operators
Group 5:	Leads, operators

consistently spending more to build a product than the product will sell for does not have three years to implement TQC/JIT.

Table 1.6 and Figure 1.13 are examples of an initial TQC/JIT schedule (from Thailand). Classroom overload and line shutdown are minimized through the use of such staggered schedules.

Closed-Loop Data Collection, Analysis, and Reporting

Most companies are inundated with data. This is primarily due to the fact that computers can literally produce more output than was input. Of critical concern with any data system is the data's usefulness. The term *closed-loop* implies that data are consistently used to control a

Statement of Problem: Implementation Group Training

Name of FIT/CAT: Not Applicable

Leader/Members: See Team List

Total Quality System

Implementation Action Items and Corrective Action Plan

Activity	Person Respons	Feb 1 2 3 4	March 1 2 3 4	April 1 2 3 4	May 1 2 3 4	June 1 2 3 4	July 1 2 3 4	Aug 1 2 3 4	Sept 1 2 3 4	Status
Course A	Yong		1 2 3 4 5							
Course B				1 2 3 4 5						
Course C					1 2 3 4 5					
Course D						1 2 3 4 5				

Figure 1.13

process. The closer data collection comes to being real-time, the quicker process adjustments can be made. Regardless of how real-time data are, however, if the data are not fed back to those who can use them most, little corrective action can be expected.

In order for a data system to assist in the prevention of defects and lost time, the people most directly able to change the process must have feedback on how they are doing their jobs. Furthermore, regardless of who collects and analyzes the data, the feedback should be provided in a timely manner and in a format that is easily interpreted.[19] That is, the feedback they receive should leave no doubt as to whether or not they are doing their jobs properly.

Most data systems have been developed for managers, not operators. While many levels of management should receive various production, efficiency, and quality summaries, the people in most need of individualized feedback (e.g., assemblers) cannot see the relevance of management level summary reports. Line personnel should receive rapid feedback which shows them how they are doing.

The impact that trendlines can have on teamwork and motivation cannot be underestimated. CAT and FIT teams depend on monitoring changes in their processes as they attempt corrective and preventive actions.[16] Positive changes in trend lines show the team they have found a substantial cause and have done a good job. Motivation and teamwork are enhanced for attempting the next round of improvement.

Organization

A preventive system does not depend on hoards of inspectors. A trend line comparing the ratio of inspectors to operators should be prepared with the objective of reducing the ratio in mind. As teams develop in an organization, the number of inspectors should decrease. This also shows up as equipment, space, inventory, rework, and hours per unit reductions.

Most companies have strong, centralized quality organizations which include inspection, quality engineering, test, audit, calibration, reliability, etc. A preventive quality system is one in which, over time, the responsibility for quality is integrated throughout the entire company. In a TQC/JIT system, under the guidance of a top-level team (TLT), the CATs and FITs identify, monitor, analyze, and correct problems. The implication is that planning for the integration of personnel with the "quality" title must be accomplished in anticipation of process improvements. As increasing numbers of CATs and FITs are implemented, and as each individual assumes responsibility for the quality of each job, fewer overhead personnel will be required.

Vendor Liaison

Obviously, the prevention of material quality disasters is best handled at the vendor's site and depends on the vendor's ability to prevent problems.

If a checklist was developed that consisted of questions such as might be posed from implementation of the aforementioned sections, a new type of vendor evaluation methodology would result. Each vendor would be evaluated in terms of the degree to which they had implemented, or planned to implement, various components of a preventive TQC/JIT system. The vendor with a low rating could be considered high risk. Clearly, the vendor who exhibits no formal preventive program efforts is not in a good position to prevent problems. Conversely, the customer who does not evaluate vendors with regard to their preventive capabilities should not expect their vendors to prevent problems.

Customer Interface

Since external failures or customer returns represent the most costly type of quality failures, some preventive mechanisms are necessary at the customer's end. To accomplish this, process capabilities must be statistically determined and compared to customer specifications prior to production, not later, when the customer wants to return out-of-spec product. Potential problems must be highlighted and negotiated with the customer up front. The timing and information are to be used in the design for manufacture and design reviews with the customer present.

Customers also can be provided with process control charts, process capability data, and correlation parts and data to help them understand and correct problems. This implies that the vendor company is attempting to implement continuous improvement as required by TQC/JIT systems. Sending a customer out-of-control data with no action plan can be dangerous. Many companies are fearful of these suggested data sharing recommendations, and this attitude reflects a lack of dedication to preventing problems.

Final product auditors benefit greatly from visiting customers and studying how shipments will be physically audited at receiving inspection, what is required to achieve dock-to-stock status, and the specifics of measurement, inspection, and test. Such activities are preventive in nature and help eliminate product returns.

SUMMARY

This chapter provided an overview of the basic TQC/JIT terms and concepts.

Any given company probably has some of the coordinated body of methods necessary for a preventive TQC/JIT system. It is important that each of the methods be recognized as preventive in nature, treated as a part of a system, and are refined and added to in the future.

No company could realistically expect to immediately implement all aspects of TQC/JIT discussed throughout this book. Development of the organization and planning for implementation are critical next steps.

Regardless of the time line, companies must take specific steps to achieve the quality and throughput levels of which they are capable and required to achieve in order to compete successfully. The fact that many countries' companies have successfully implemented

TQC/JIT systems removes the excuse that "It can't be done here."

An organization consisting of a top-level team (TLT), corrective action teams (CATs), and functional improvement teams (FITs) is developed to manage (Chapter 2) and implement (Chapter 3) the system. On demand, other specialized teams are assigned (Chapter 4). All teams focus their efforts on cost savings through quality and throughput improvements (Chapter 5).

2

Organizational and Team Concepts

*T*his chapter outlines how a company can organize the teams required to implement and support a TQC/JIT system. As stated in Chapter 1, there are three main types of teams that need to be developed in order to implement the steps outlined in Table 1.3.

THE TOP-LEVEL TEAM

The top-level team consisting mainly of top-level managers (but mixed with a few nonmanagerial personnel for balance) is the first group to be established. The choice of persons to become team members should be discussed openly throughout the organization. The purpose of this team should be made clear to all personnel. This team will plan and manage system implementation. There is work involved. All potential team candidates should have received introductory training and should understand the concepts discussed in Chapter 1.

Obviously, there will be attempts by quick-thinking, top-level managers to load this team with favorite sons and daughters. Such is the nature of organizational politics. Likewise, some managers will want to stack the team with assassins, malcontents, nonbelievers, etc. Organizers should beware of such political maneuvering. Probably, the simplest advice is to choose members who are basically honest and motivated to do a good quality improvement job. Generally, such people are abundant in any organization. They tend to be visible through their frustration with dealing with the status quo. Sometimes they are vocal in their demands that the job be done correctly. Such people make champions and their selection helps broadcast the message that "change is coming."

Figure 2.1 is an example of a small organization from which nine members have been selected to serve on the top-level TQC/JIT team. Team members are indicated by an asterisk.

Unfortunately, something must be mentioned about female employees. Most organizations tend to shy away from making women part of top-level management. This practice often is carried over into new organizational developments such as required by TQC/JIT. Such practices are observed worldwide. In the United States, such practices are illegal and unethical. Other cultures must decide for themselves, but there is no place in a 100 percent employee involvement program for such prejudiced behavior. Each individual's input and brain power is valuable and required.

Further ideas concerning top-level team member selection can be gained by reading the section on "Problems Involved with the Delegation of Authority and Responsibility" on page 84.

The size of the team is not critical. Nine is a good minimum number but the team should not exceed 12. A team of six highly dedicated and committed people can handle the job. Persons already working 18 hours per day should probably be excluded because they won't have the time even if they are motivated.

The mix of the team members is critical. Input is required from as many departments and job functions as possible. All members of this team have one vote regardless of rank outside of the meeting room. This implies that the chief executive officer, president, some

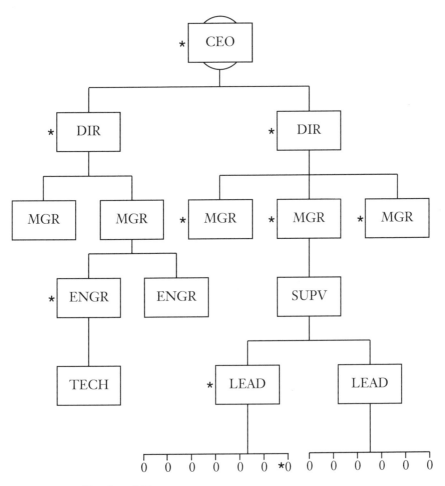

Figure 2.1   Top-Level Team

vice presidents, some directors, some managers, a lead or two, an accountant, a secretary, and even a line operator might be invited. Each company must examine its current organization to select a balanced team. A vice president of operations cannot adequately represent people on the line.

The top-level system management team has carried various titles at different companies. Some titles previously used are Quality Challenge Team (QCT), Quality Improvement Team (QIT), and Quality Management Team (QMT). Be creative.

Table 2.1 contains a list of the team's primary responsibilities.

Table 2.1   Top-Level Team Responsibilities

1. Define and use the TQC/JIT organizational structure.
2. Write and manage a plan for system implementation and maintenance. This plan should include the following:
   A. Determine ways for all individuals to attain personal dedication and commitment to TQC/JIT principles and practices.
   B. Establish a method to keep people informed of system activities, successes, and efforts.
   C. Develop policies which hold all personnel accountable for their dedication to TQC/JIT implementation.
   D. Provide a means for showing appreciation for outstanding accomplishments.
   E. Define how system, team, and individual activities and results will be made visible and shared.
   F. Determine how motivational levels will be perpetuated throughout time, through thick and thin, through successes and failures.
3. Oversee and manage implementation activities (Table 1.3).

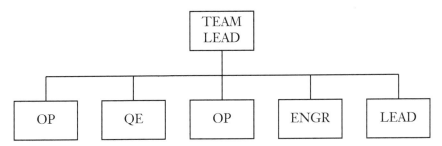

Figure 2.2   Cross-Functional Corrective Action Teams (CATs)

Generally, after the top-level team is trained in basic TQC/JIT, members selected, and the overall goal of the team clear, the first task of the team is to establish and communicate an overall organization consistent with TQC/JIT team formation and with the current organization. Recall that in addition to the top-level team, CATs and FITs are required. Previously it was recommended that the top-level team consist of a mix of individuals who adequately represent top management and lower-level functions. CATs were defined as cross-functional and consisting of members from the variety of functions required to interface in order to solve a particular problem (e.g., Figure 2.2). FITs are functional in both nature and membership and direct their efforts at problems within control of the particular function (e.g., Figure 2.3).

The teams recommended in Figure 2.3 are the types of CATs focused on implementation of specific activities required to support JIT.

Although Figures 2.1, 2.2, and 2.3 provide some insight into the structure of different teams, the mechanism for connecting teams throughout the organization needs clarification.

Figure 2.4 depicts a top-level team with each managerial member heading up a functional level team. In this partial organizational chart, a regular organization is depicted with a president, three vice presidents, three directors, and three managers. Naturally, many more people could be shown, but for illustration purposes the chart is complete.

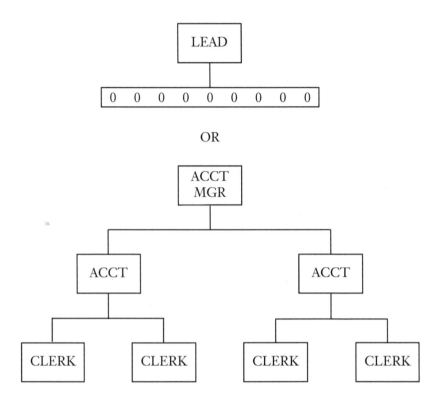

Figure 2.3   Functional Teams

The president, two vice presidents, and director number 2 make up the TLT to which three CATs report directly (circle A). An FIT is shown in circle B. Vice president number 1 and three directors meet weekly to address problems at their level. Notice that vice president number 1 is a member of the top-level team and is also responsible for implementation of the FIT in circle B. This FIT contains vice president number 1's normal direct reports. In this manner, there is little confusion as to how FITs are structured. This should not imply that vice president number 1 will be the leader of the FIT B. Also notice that director 1 is a member of FIT B and a member or leader of FIT C.

The linkage established by dual responsibilities in higher- and lower-level FITs ensures that information and needs will flow in both directions. Problems that lower-level teams cannot solve due to some type of barrier are communicated to the next higher level FIT during FIT meetings. Manager-level FITs are responsible for the removal of barriers to lower-level problem situations.

Suppose, for example, that manager 3 attended FIT meetings with members of the next lower FIT (not shown). Now, suppose this FIT was working on a problem to reduce paperwork bottlenecks and planned to redesign several forms into one simple form. The redesign requires reprinting of forms which in turn requires some budget modification. Without consideration and approval by FIT C, this lower-level team might not solve their problem. The inability of the lower-level team to overcome the need for funds is known as a *barrier* and it is the responsibility of the next higher level FIT to address and help remove that barrier. In this case, manager 3, as a member of both FIT C and the FIT, carries this request to the next meeting of FIT C. The request becomes an agenda item and must be addressed by FIT C. Director-level and above FIT meetings often focus on removing barriers to lower-level accomplishments. This is an application of W. E. Deming's barrier removal concept presented in his book, *Quality, Productivity, and Competitive Position.*[25]

With the organization defined and understood by the top-level

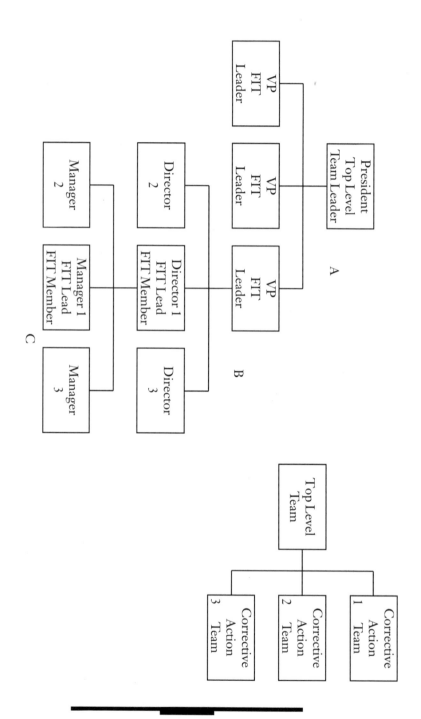

Figure 2.4 Organizational Integration

team, a management plan must be written.

Each member of the top-level team should volunteer for or be assigned a planning and implementation item from Table 2.1, items 2A through 3 for which to write a plan. The following discussion follows the format of Table 2.1. To complete the planning cycle by the top-level team, the team leader should specify who is responsible for each part of the plan and when that part of the plan is due for presentation to other team members.

Recall that the first test of top-level team commitment came when the team was organized to include non-managerial members. The second test of commitment is whether or not top-level team members complete their plans on time. This planning cycle should take between 30 and 60 days. Many organizations compress this cycle. Each organization must make its own decision regarding the time allowed for planning.

An example of a complete plan is presented in Appendix A. Appendix B includes an example of a basic GANTT planning chart which will be referred to throughout all planning sections in this book.

2A. Determine ways for all individuals to attain personal dedication and commitment to TQC/JIT principles and practices.

First, a corporate TQC/JIT policy should be written and publicized. Figures 2.5 and 2.6 contain sample policies written by two U.S. companies. Figure 2.5 contains a policy that is more briefly stated and directed at quality than that of Figure 2.6, which illustrates both quality and JIT statements. Both contain statements of basic elements and attitudes outlined in Chapter 1. Both are strong and deliberate statements to which all organizational members are expected to comply.

The top-level team responsible for the policy in Figure 2.5 also has added a statement that is used on all company communications, and indeed, even on operator smocks: "Committed to Quality." Many companies use such statements to further compress and clarify

The company is committed to quality performance from every employee.

Our standard for products and service is zero defects.

Our ultimate goal is total customer satisfaction achieved by constantly improving quality, delivery, and service.

Figure 2.5   The Company Quality Policy "Committed to Quality"

- We will support customers by exceeding customer requirements and specifications.
- We are committed to total top management and employee quality performance.
- We will keep customers satisfied by providing quality products, delivery, and service.
- We will constantly improve quality by implementing companywide total quality (TQC) in all areas using just-in-time (JIT) strategies.
- Our target is "zero defects" (ZD).
- We will achieve cost savings in all areas by simplifying, combining, and eliminating process steps.
- We are dedicated to the prevention of problems.
- We believe quality must be built into the process, not inspected in.
- We will demand quality consciousness at all levels.
- We believe every idea is valuable for quality improvements.

Figure 2.6   "Quality Excellence"

the overall organizational goal. For example, Ford Motor Company uses "Quality is Job 1." Many other statements can be seen and heard through daily advertising.

Attaining dedication and commitment to TQC/JIT principles and practices means a great deal more than the generation of policies and statements. When writing this section of the plan, the TLT should discuss and list how the members will show that they are committed to the TQC/JIT system. In this sense, commitment means to act in ways which are consistent with TQC/JIT policies. The act in support of the policy is the manner in which commitment and dedication will become visible to all organizational members.

For example, the statement that "We will support customers by exceeding customer requirements and specifications" can be interpreted to mean that requirements and specifications will be carefully defined and agreed on and that, in a manufacturing environment, process capabilities (Chapter 3) will exceed the commonly accepted 1.33 level. This implies that a never-ending engineering, quality, and production effort will be launched to improve tooling and design.

Similar interpretations can be made for internal customers. For example, if a draftsperson cannot understand an engineer's scribble on a drawing due for revision, both parties are in jeopardy. The engineer's drawing will either be rejected or done incorrectly by the draftsperson, thus causing cost and lead time increases in the form of rework. The draftsperson will have to spend extra time trying to decipher what the engineer wanted. Either rework or re-interpretation efforts can cause other work to pile up, thus increasing cycle time through the drafting unit. Both losses are avoidable if engineers and draftspersons clearly understand the other's requirements and are dedicated to first-time quality. To act in other ways indicates a lack of commitment and dedication.

From a management point of view, managers must recognize their customers and work to help the functional improvement team (FIT) define their customers' requirements through FIT activities. Such demonstrated dedication on the part of the group manager is a good indication of true leadership as each FIT member comes to define their own customers and their customers' requirements as part of their daily job. This level of managerial involvement demonstrates that managers are actively involved in helping FITs to use TQC/JIT tools to improve quality and reduce throughput times.

All managers in all departments must participate.

As work moves from customer to customer within an organization (e.g., Figure 2.7), interFIT support begins to develop and feelings that one team is trying to dump work on the other teams diminish. With proper training of all members of all teams, an understanding develops that all organizational persons are in this together and that one department is not another's enemy. Each department and person has at least one vendor and one customer. Most have more than one.

In one United States company a single customer service FIT decided to attack the problem of "excessive time required to process customer quotes." This team used basic tools (process flowcharting; cycle, cost, or defect analysis; control charting; causal analysis; and corrective action). Inspired by the results of preliminary data collection efforts, the FIT leader set up a meeting with three other FIT leaders and described the problem and findings. The several FITs involved in the quote cycle stream decided to cooperate in the development of a clean set of requirements and flow. In a brief period, the quote cycle time through the company and the error-associated quote error rates were reduced to less than 10 percent of the original. By working together, the customer service, sales, engineering, document control, and purchasing FITs had solved a problem which had existed for years. The leader of the customer service FIT was given the company's highest TQC/JIT improvement award for this leadership effort.

Commitment was demonstrated in two ways. FIT members all learned, cooperated, and solved the problem. Managers supported

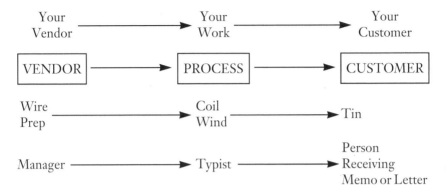

Figure 2.7   Work Movement from Customer to Customer

the effort through their respective departments.

Actions speak louder than words.

Figure 2.8 is an example of one company's attempt to operationalize commitment (example from Thailand). The information summarized in Figure 2.8 was developed by the company's TLT during a single brainstorming session. Such ideas could be included in any organization's dedication and commitment plan.

Commitment can be demonstrated in many subtle ways which transmit powerful messages. A TLT which refuses to allow interruptions during TLT meetings is telling the outside world that this meeting is the most important event of the moment. Nothing supercedes the meeting's intent. Secretaries and direct reports rarely find it difficult to accept the fact that the boss is not to be disturbed. It is more likely that disagreement with such a rule will come from certain TLT members. Adamant disagreement is a clear indication of a lack of commitment. Asking the TLT members to discuss the issue of "no interruptions" is a good way to feel out those who would rather be somewhere else. Similarly, TLT members who arrive late at meetings or fail to attend are demonstrating that the effort is of secondary importance.

Commitment means to:

1. Share authority and responsibility.

2. Listen to others' opinions and let others try their ideas.

3. Solve problems for lower-level teams that they cannot solve themselves.

4. Help others to plan and budget for continuous improvement.

5. Attend meetings and complete action items.

6. Manage the planning and implementation of the TQC/JIT system.

7. Stop shipments of defective materials.

8. Continuously challenge others to simplify, combine, and eliminate in order to control the seven wastes.

Figure 2.8   Element: Commitment

2B. Establish a method to keep people informed of system activities, successes, and efforts.

The importance of communicating TQC/JIT efforts cannot be overemphasized. First, common problems often find common solutions. If one FIT has recognized a problem and has solved it, another FIT in another place may be able to use that knowledge to quickly solve a similar problem. Why re-invent the wheel? Second, hidden managerial and nonmanagerial expertise and knowledge cannot be brought into action without familiarity with current efforts and problems. Many people throughout an organization have faced similar problems at other times in their careers and have found simple, effective solutions. This resource must be tapped and transferred to less-experienced persons.

There is a third reason for open communication of system status and activities, and it may be positively or negatively viewed by players. External customers are becoming increasingly aware of the managerial power of TQC/JIT systems. Many of the largest and most successful American corporations intentionally search for vendors capable of identifying and continually solving problems. This can be easily verified by asking for the company's vendor qualification procedures. Vendors who cannot demonstrate such ongoing, visible, and honest efforts are scratched from potential vendor lists. Meanwhile, sales personnel from these vendors continue to wonder why they cannot get an order from such large customers. This does not imply that a TQC/JIT system should be pushed for the sole purpose of improving sales through phony efforts. Employees and customers are quick to detect such deceptions. A shipment rejected at the back door and shipped anyway, only to be rejected by the customer, quickly conveys the truth about managerial intent. Employees with knowledge of such activities (and the word spreads rapidly) will treat later TQC/JIT efforts with dedication congruent with that of the actions of managers demanding such shipments.

Some managers are afraid to publish the fact that problems exist in areas under their control in the same way that some line leads do not like control charts visible on their lines. Such attitudes often reflect operational realities. In many companies a manager with an internal problem that becomes public is taken advantage of by others wanting to escape blame for their own problems. Politics and power struggles come into play. In these cases, managers quickly learn to keep problems from public scrutiny, a practice that undermines TQC/JIT efforts.

Open identification and discussion of power play occurrences should be encouraged in order to reveal true intentions. Planning for such potentially heated discussions helps reduce their undermining effects.

The TLT is responsible for management of the TQC/JIT system. Management of any aspect of an organization requires information relative to operational status. This part of the plan should include the development and implementation of a reporting system that delivers pertinent information to the TLT. Most FIT and CAT activities can be easily tracked using a traditional filing system. A simple graph (Figure 2.9) can be used to show the number of TLTs (if multiple facilities are involved), FITs, and CATs operational at any point in time.

Table 2.2 is an example of how specific teams may be tracked and reported using a basic LOTUS 1-2-3™ file. This file should include the name and nature of the team, the level of implementation (identify, monitor, analysis, corrective action), the team leader's name, the meeting time, and an abbreviation of the problem being addressed. Other suggested reports include: the percent of persons involved (number of people on teams divided by the total number in the organization times 100), cost savings summaries by department, division or team, and overall team summary reports (Figure 2.10).

Figure 2.10 is an excellent example of a team summary report. In this case, a team at a Hewlett-Packard plant recognized that a manufacturing line was down an average of 15 hours per month due to a lack of materials. They flowcharted the materials delivery process, analyzed the problem for potential causes (Ishikawa diagram), defined and implemented a data collection strategy, and implemented corrective action.[9] Over a six-month period, production hours lost due to process interruptions were reduced to near zero. This could be translated to mean that the line was operational for an average of 15 hours per month more than without corrective action (almost a 9 percent improvement in productivity).

The TLT plan should include statements of how information will be shared among employees. Some companies publish newsletters on a quarterly basis. Others publish results on specially designated walls throughout the facility. Another approach is to hold monthly or bimonthly team leader meetings in which each team leader describes the status of team activities, thereby allowing for an open forum for discussion. Team leaders are expected to convey some of this information back to their own teams. In some cases, CAT leaders (and members) are invited into the TLT meetings to present summaries.

Regardless of what medium is used to report team status, the reporting forms and system should be kept simple. The intent is not to develop a paper monster, but to communicate significant results.

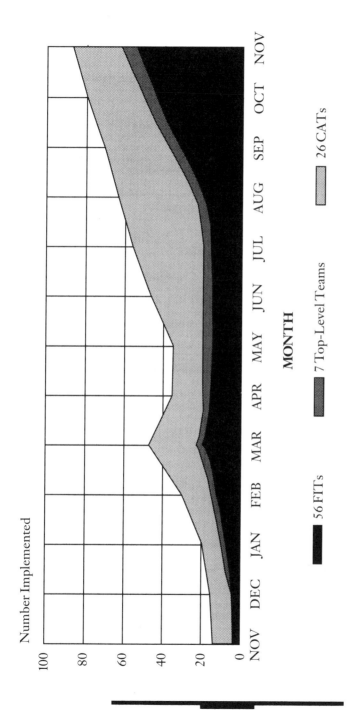

Figure 2.9 TQC Team Implementation Tracking

Table 2.2 Team Tracking and Status Report

Name of Team	Status Phase				Leader	Meeting Time	Main Goal
	A	B	C	D			
Top-Level Team	Non Applicable to TLT Activities				RBM	1pm Mon	System Implementation and Management
Corrective Action Teams							
Supplier Management	X	X	X		R. Klimo	10:30 Mon	Improve Vendor Performance
Excess Inventory	X	X	X	X	BG	7 am Thurs	Reduce Excess Inventory
Glass Stains	X				RC	8:30 Wed	Reduce Stains from Current Level
Functional Improvement Teams							
Secretary FIT	X	X			D. Boggs	9 am Tues	Improve Copier Efficiency and Quality
Engineering FIT	X	X	X	X	PW	10 am Tues	Reduce Documentation Errors
Customer Service FIT	X				B. Murray	8 am Thurs	Reduce Sales Order Cycle Time and Defects

Team						Leader	Time	Objective
Purchasing FIT	X	X	X	X	X	R. Klimo	7:30 Fri	Improve Quality of Requisitions
Quality Engineering FIT	X	X	X	X	X	J. Fish	10 am Wed	Reduce Planning Defects (Corporate)
JIT Line A FIT	X	X	X	X		B. Yong	1pm Tues	Reduce Lint in Coil Defects
JIT Line C FIT	X		X			P. Tipa	2 pm Tues	Reduce Chip Defects
Special Teams								
KANBAN Team						H. Wong	8 am Tues	Rebalance JIT Line A
Setup Team						G. Knodel	8 am Fri	Reduce Tester Setup Times
SPC Team						K. Gangkai	4 pm Mon	Move SPC In-Line for JIT Line F

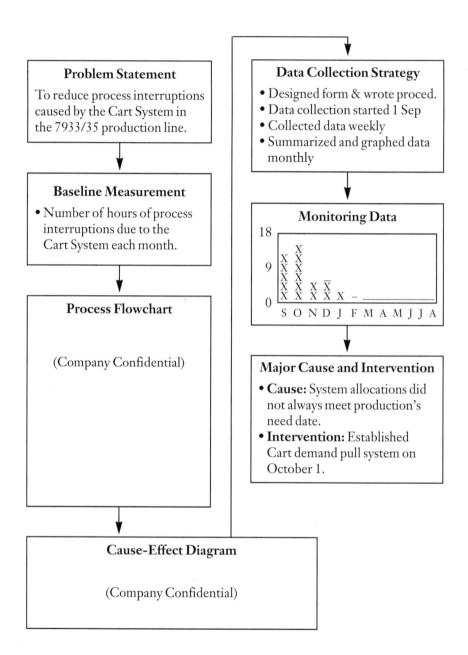

Figure 2.10   7933/35 Cart System TQC Storyboard

Each team's monthly report should be no longer than one page. This report should be filed with a cleaner summary prepared for the TLT (Figures 2.9 and 2.10 and Table 2.2).

Many other methods for summarizing and reporting the TQC/JIT system results have been used. The TLT member responsible for planning and managing **2B.** activities might do well to talk to other TLT members for additional ideas since each member may have different report format ideas.

2C. Develop policies that hold all personnel accountable for their dedication to TQC/JIT implementation.

Most companies today use some form of management-by-objectives (MBO) to control plan implementation. A TQC/JIT system is no different. In truth, any form of MBO control may be used to ensure that the objectives (and hopefully, activities) of all personnel are reasonably in line with departmental and company goals.

For purposes of this discussion, goals are global statements which determine direction. Objectives are specific statements, written with clarity, which tell how an individual will attack his/her part toward attaining the overall goal. Recall that the purpose of TQC/JIT is continuous improvement in cost reductions associated with wasted time and rework. Depending on position and responsibility, each individual in the organization is expected to set direction toward accomplishing, to work toward, and to accomplish some specific activity or set of activities that will help the overall organization attain the goal.

The formalization of the thought process whereby objectives are designed to help reach goals is not new. Nor is the thought that individuals and groups are accountable for completion of those objectives and attainment of goals. In some companies, employees are said to be accountable for their output and the success of their efforts. Since TQC/JIT generally represents the setting of major organizational goals, individuals demanding pay for their services should be held accountable for the attainment or nonattainment of their objectives. Table 2.3 represents one Thailand company's attempt to develop an *Accountability Policy*. This policy is included as a sample to help reduce other companies' efforts in the development of a similar policy. (Forms included for guidance in the implementation of this policy are found in Appendix C.)

Table 2.3   Accountability Policy

A. Policy

The company emphasizes each employee's acceptance of personal responsibility for carrying out work-related duties on schedule, within established budgets and with error-free quality. To clearly establish such individual accountability, company policy provides for documented agreements between supervisors and employees regarding an employee's certain work performance objectives. Such agreements are made annually at the beginning of each year. Other accountability agreements may also be made between leaders of specific interdepartmental CAT/project teams and members of each team; such teams and project accountability agreements occur periodically depending on operational requirements.

B. Definitions

1. Performance Agreement: A documented commitment between a supervisor and employee establishing work-performance objectives. Such written objectives must be agreed on between the supervisor and the employee. They should be written in specific and measurable terms and should indicate when completion is required.

(Table 2.3 continued)

(Table 2.3 continued)

C. Administration

1. During January of each year, supervisors and employees at all levels of the company establish performance agreements and document them on individual objectives forms (Appendix C) provided for that purpose.

   a. Completed individual objectives forms are reviewed by the next management level to ensure consistency with department goals.

   b. A copy of each employee's individual objectives form is forwarded by the supervisor of the personnel department for inclusion in the employee's personnel file.

2. During the first month of each succeeding quarter, all supervisors meet individually with employees to review and discuss progress during the prior quarter toward achieving performance objectives. At this time, individual objectives may be modified in accordance with changed operating conditions.

   a. Supervisors rate progress on the individual objectives' form and provide corrective action, direction, or support, as required.

   b. Supervisors as FIT leaders report overall unit progress to the TLT through written summaries and/or verbal presentations as requested by the TLT. Noteworthy individual problems and achievements should be highlighted at that time.

   c. Upon completion of the year-end quarter performance objectives review, completed individual objectives forms are again reviewed by the next higher management level and forwarded to the personnel department for inclusion

(Table 2.3 continued)

(Table 2.3 continued)

in the employee's personnel file and consideration in overall performance appraisal.

3. CAT/Project teams may be formed periodically as required by the TLT or operating management. Upon CAT/Project formation, the designated team leader is accountable for establishing a project performance agreement among the team members. Such agreement should include a project objective, component activities, milestone dates, and team member accountability for completion of the project. A CAT/Project objectives form (Appendix C) is provided for this purpose. All team members must note their acceptance of accountability for the CAT/Project plan in the space provided on the form.

a. The TLT management requires periodic CAT/Project status reviews. Scheduled reviews may occur weekly, monthly, or quarterly depending on the nature of the activity, and they may involve written or verbal presentations. The CAT/Project leader is accountable for maintaining current status information and for coordinating status review presentations.

b. CAT/Project team leaders monitor team member performance and advise the TLT regarding noteworthy performance. At the direction of the TLT, such recognition may be recorded in an employee's personnel file for consideration in overall performance appraisal.

The implementation of an accountability policy is likely to cause resistance in some companies. Generally people do not like to be nailed down regarding their commitments, and have a difficult time understanding why such a procedure is necessary. Every excuse possible

(Table 2.3 continued)

(Table 2.3 continued)

will be heard for delays in the implementation of an accountability policy. Management must quickly implement this system and must consistently follow up to ensure 100 percent implementation.

D. Provide a means for showing appreciation for outstanding accomplishments.

The plan written for rewarding people for significant TQC/JIT contributions will guide FIT and CAT leaders in their efforts to keep motivation at a high level. Several alternatives can be recommended. The plan must encompass different levels and types of rewards.

Champions should be promoted. Remember that in Chapter 1 the concept of enduring organizational change was discussed and the fact that forced change would not endure was pointed out. This can be interpreted to mean that strong positive reinforcement is required where mandatory implementation is not demanded. There is no more powerful motivator to implementation than to announce to the world that a person has won a raise or promotion for successful TQC/JIT work. On the other hand, those who do not support TQC/JIT should not be promoted or rewarded.

Individuals as well as team efforts should be considered. Generally, a team which successfully solves a costly problem should be considered to have saved the company money (hopefully, substantial amounts). Team awards could include placing names on a perpetual trophy or plaque, as well as a team dinner. Individual awards often include TQC/JIT "champion" pins or cups, and should be followed up with a certificate of appreciation and a letter of appreciation placed in the personnel file.

Some organizations will tie the appreciation for excellent

(Table 2.3 continued)

(Table 2.3 continued)

TQC/JIT efforts to raises and promotions. Linked with the accountability effort described in paragraph C, a powerful subsystem can be developed.

Each organization must face the question of providing financial rewards to individuals or teams which solve problems. Some attitudes often restrict the use of financial rewards. If managers believe financial rewards should not be used because "It's their job anyway," then this same attitude should affect managerial bonuses and profit sharing. This may sound tough, but employees generally know when bonuses and profits are shared only among the elite. Such circumstances are not good for employee motivation.

The size and type of a financial reward may vary from a few dollars or a gift certificate to more significant figures. As is the case with any type of award, individual players who have consistently supported the TQC/JIT effort through exemplary effort, could be recognized with dinner for two or even a weekend in some resort.

All rewards should be presented publicly. Often, the public recognition surrounding the award is more important to the individual than the reward's substance. If there is a single overwhelming feeling among employees in large companies, it is that their efforts are not appreciated or recognized. Public recognition by a boss or a significant company officer helps morale tremendously. The feeling that someone does give a damn and cares, and that such efforts are needed and appreciated is critical to any human.

Bestowal of the award with sincerity often is difficult for some managers. Men, in general, and, more specifically, male bosses, are not known for their compassion. Probably the greatest single cause for turnovers in an organization is the lack of humane

(Table 2.3 continued)

(Table 2.3 continued)

contact between employees and bosses. Words that may be substituted for humane include kind, merciful, tender, sympathetic, and civilized. Certainly, others observing the award presentation will feel proud for the recipient and will leave with a point of view more likely to motivate than undermine.

The bottom line to any plan for a show of appreciation is that such shows must be frequent, visible, and justified.

E. Define how system, team, and individual activities and results will be made visible and shared.

Communication of system efforts and accomplishments across departmental and organizational boundaries is required. A formal communication plan must be written and implemented.

In the simplest form, a semimonthly newsletter with a catchy title will be fun to read. People like to see their names in print, read about their efforts, and read articles which they wrote. Articles should come from team members. There is no need to form a separate administrative group to publish the results. A desktop computer with a word processor and some graphic capabilities works fine. Short frequent newsletters seem to be better than long infrequent ones. Two sides of one page often is enough and can be cheaply printed and distributed to all employees in the company mail. Publication priority should be given to teams showing cost savings as a result of their efforts.

The newsletter could contain articles about individuals or teams, goals and accomplishments, and should include articles about failures. Remember, the newsletter is to communicate failed corrective action attempts may help another team not to take the same approach, thereby increasing their probability for success.

(Table 2.3 continued)

(Table 2.3 continued)

Quarterly meetings including all team leaders is another good means of communication. Each team leader can be given 10 minutes to present the team problem, data, analysis, and current results or corrective action attempts. Team leaders attending such meetings should be encouraged to share results with their respective teams during the next regularly scheduled meeting. Some team leaders choose to provide other team leaders with written summaries.

Chapter 3 contains other means of communicating team status up and down the organization. The Standard Minutes Form is used to establish meeting agendas and summarize action items. This form is to be forwarded to the system manager for filing and summarization in the monthly system status report reviewed by the TLT. The monthly system status report (Chapter 3) is a public document which can be delivered to team leaders semimonthly.

The team status file kept by the system manager should be an open file. This means that other team members should have access to any document in the file. Occasions arise when one team, upon hearing that another is working on a problem, will want to review how certain activities were handled. The file should be considered public property and should be placed where it is accessible to interested parties. Each team in each division should have complete activities documentation on file. A TLT file and plan also should be included. It is an easy task to color-code files to visually separate CAT and FIT files.

The system organizational structure (TLT, CAT, FIT) establishes successfully and easily used communications routes. Recall that each manager is a member of two FITs. A manager attends FIT meetings with direct reports and also attends a higher level FIT as a direct report to a higher level manager. Barriers that

(Table 2.3 continued)

(Table 2.3 continued)

are identified in lower level FITs should be discussed and disposi-
tioned or acted on by the higher level FIT. Again, this is a normal
communications route in any organization without the
TQC/JIT organization suggested here. There should be little
resistance to such communication although meeting focus must
be maintained. Quality and work flow problem solutions are
the only priorities.

Some organizations hold quarterly status review meetings
as a standard method of communicating with employees.
Such meetings are a good time to communicate successful
TQC/JIT efforts and to distribute awards. This type of activity
ties the system communication effort in with the appreciation effort.

**F. Determine how motivational levels will be perpetuated
through time, through thick and thin, through successes
and failures.**

Over time, implementation of TQC/JIT systems goes
through various stages of motivation and activity.

Usually, stage one is training oriented. During this stage,
upper management receives introductory training, forms the
TLT, and writes the implementation plan.

Stage two continues training to lower levels. This stage normally requires several months to one year. As people become
trained in implementation techniques, CATs and FITs are
formed and become operational. During this stage, motivation
is high. This is especially true if the TLT demonstrates commitment and dedication by becoming involved and managing the
system. Coupled with good communications and a reward
structure, an increasing number of teams join the effort and
problems begin to be solved.

(Table 2.3 continued)

(Table 2.3 continued)

Stage three begins to take hold after several months to one year. The system starts to slow down, other priorities begin to get in the way, meetings may be cancelled or delayed, and problem solutions seem fewer. This is the time when motivation needs a boost.

The ups and downs of motivation and problem solving appear to run in annual cycles.

The methods used to perpetuate motivational levels are varied. Some companies set up annual parties where all employees, and perhaps their families, attend activities which highlight the TQC/JIT system. The party may run all day, and include many activities including games, skits, food, and drink. Annual awards for top team and individual success are presented. Fun is the word for the day.

Such system renewal activities are intended to re-invigorate efforts. Focus is on dedication to TQC/JIT as an organizational way of life. The policy developed some months ago is renewed, resolutions are established for the new year, and all employees have a chance to examine all that was accomplished with renewed focus on the future.

The TLT member with the responsibility for planning and implementing this perpetuating component must plan and organize the activities well ahead of time.

G. Train all personnel in TQC/JIT concepts and strategies.

Training covering basic TQC/JIT concepts outlined in Chapter 1 and the specific team problem-solving tools outlined in Chapter 3 must be planned and executed on schedule. All employees should be trained. Since all employees cannot be trained at one time, however, a staggered schedule is suggested.

(Table 2.3 continued)

(Table 2.3 continued)

In order to effectively and expeditiously penetrate the organization from top to bottom, some companies have trained trainers. Three or four volunteers may be selected to intensively study the concepts and practices presented herein. Training of trainers also is available from the American Electronics Association as well as many professional private consulting groups.

3. Oversee and manage implementation activities (Table 1.3).

TQC/JIT implementation requires a two-pronged approach. First, the TLT is responsible for managing each component listed in Table 2.1. Second, CATs and FITs are responsible for implementing specific problem solutions.

After the TQC/JIT plan is written, the TLT should approve or modify each component until group acceptance is achieved. Since each activity in the plan will have a due date and a responsible person noted, it should be simple to monitor implementation. The plan should be reviewed by the TLT at least every two months. An easy way to accomplish this is to take some time from every TLT meeting to review one component of the plan. This means that the implementation of each component will be reviewed approximately every six to eight weeks.

ESTABLISHING AND RUNNING CORRECTIVE ACTION TEAMS (CATS)

Corrective action teams are selected and manpower assigned by top-level team authority. TLT members are expected to identify companywide problems, prioritize those problems, and assign CATs to solve the problems. Table 2.4 represents the responses from one corporate headquarters' TLT brainstorming session. The left-hand column lists the major problem areas while the right-hand column represents estimates of annual losses due to the problem. This list was generated from approximately 40 top managers in a corporation with annual sales of approximately $120 million. Despite obvious overestimation of financial losses, the list helped to set priorities for CAT selection and activities.

Caution must be exercised with the number of CATs authorized to be operational at any one time. Each CAT member will simultaneously be involved with at least one FIT. This means that the extra time and effort required to support CAT activities will be that much more burdensome. Generally, an organization of 200 personnel should maintain no more than three or four CATs at any one time. The number of operational CATs should, however, depend on the size of the organization and its structure.

When a CAT solves the assigned problem, the CAT is disbanded by the TLT, members recognized for their contributions, and another problem is selected from the TLT problem list for correction.

A corporate headquarters with four manufacturing sites could accommodate four CATs at each site with four more at corporate headquarters. Since identical problems often occur at multiple sites (especially in franchised service industries or multiple-site manufacturing companies), each site involved in the problem could assign one member as a member of the intersite CAT. Communications among intersite CAT members generally is by FAX, express mail, or conference calls.

As with FITs the meeting time, place, and operational guidelines for CAT activities are similar but not identical. The following section contains CAT guidelines which should be provided for each team member.

Table 2.4 Major Cost Categories

Response from Group	Estimated Annual Cost
Sale/purchase transaction incomplete	2+Million
Incorrect forecasts	2M
MIS-incorrect decision data	Huge
MIS-system transaction errors	Huge
MIS-system output vs. user needs	??
Engineering design, documentation, omission errors	1M+
Not understanding specs or requirements	5+M
Incorrect product specs	1M
Vendor quality or delivery	5+M
CFM material not received on schedule	5+M
Shipping damage	2M*
Inventory excess	2+M*
Manufacturing process symptoms (yield loss)	4+M
Scrap	??
Bent flexures	1.1M
Wire damage	.61M
ABS damage	.61M
Product returns	1.5M*
Late or missed deliveries & long throughput	1.5++M**
Customer doesn't order in lead-time	2M
Unclear lines of responsibility	Huge
Communications	Very Huge

* Indicates second time noted.
** Indicates third time noted.

CORRECTIVE ACTION TEAM (CAT) GUIDELINES

The CAT is an interdepartmental corrective action team meeting generally held at a regularly scheduled time each week. The purpose of a CAT is to identify and eliminate problems and quality barriers causing defects and cycle time excesses, thus affecting overall company profitability. Such problems or barriers are considered major problems and generally are caused or controlled by several departments. Corrective and future prevention, therefore, require a companywide team effort.

The top quality team (TQT) is responsible for reviewing such problems and elevating the problem to CAT status. The TQT usually controls the number of CATs functioning at any one time.

Typical CAT agenda items include:

- Monitoring and reviewing defect and cycle time tracking charts.
- Participatively setting long-term goals or activity objectives for defect or time reduction.
- Participatively planning actions to reach the long-term goals.
- Reviewing progress to goals and action plans.
- Assigning corrective action responsibilities.
- Holding quality barrier discussions.
- Reviewing and updating defect logs.
- Providing training in problem-solving methods.

Each CAT selects a leader. The leader's responsibilities include:

- Schedule and hold CAT meetings.
- Ensure that all CAT members are trained in TQC/JIT strategies and techniques.
- Certify all CAT members to ensure their competencies in helping to implement TQC.
- Take a leadership role in discussions related to CAT functioning.

- Ensure that the CAT focuses on one clearly defined issue or problem at a time.
- Ensure that lateral accountability is maintained.
- Ensure that CAT meeting minutes are kept, reviewed, and forwarded to the TQT.
- Report the status of the CAT to the TQT.
- Forward important CAT issues, ideas, and concerns to the TQT.
- Reward CAT members for their contributions.
- Keep the group on the road of continuous quality and time-reduction improvement.

CAT members have the following responsibilities:

- Attend and actively participate in all CAT meetings.
- Ensure that all action items are completed on time with quality performance and *zero defects.*
- Identify and report quality barriers.
- Identify and report quality costs.
- Maintain records which reflect CAT progress toward solving chosen quality problems.
- Monitor all defect or cycle time charts and take immediate corrective action on out of control conditions.

The general procedure for operation of the CAT is as follows. Techniques designed to support specific steps are presented in Chapter 4.

1. Select a meeting time and place.
2. Inform all functional personnel of the time, place, and purpose of the CAT meeting.

3. During the first meeting, review the elements of the TQC/JIT system, select a leader, secretary, and review and further define the problem assigned by the TQT. Introduce CAT members to standard report formats (GANTT chart for plans and control charts for tracking, see Chapter 3).

4. Clarify the major problem area for attack. Choose one part of the problem that can be solved in a reasonably short period of time (first round).

5. Determine a method for measuring the current status of the problem. Begin data collection and chart the average reject rate, cost trend, or time to complete (JIT-variable). This trend chart will later reflect the success or failure of each corrective action attempt. The chart will be presented to the TQT on a quarterly basis along with the GANTT chart described below (item 8).

6. Based on the current average, set a goal for improvement. This may be defect reduction, yield improvement, cycle time reduction, or any variable chosen.

7. Using standard Ishikawa diagramming methods, identify specific causal relationships and as a group, choose (plan) one problem solution attempt for the first round of corrective action. Analyze defects and rework loops which cause lost time using standard TQC/JIT tools (Chapter 3).

8. Write the plan on a standard GANTT chart, and set activity objectives, including the person responsible and the date due. The GANTT charted plan will be used to make presentations to the TQT along with the trend or control chart developed in step 5.

9. Begin the implementation of your plan and review and adjust the implementation during each weekly CAT. Update the GANTT chart during each meeting.

10. As meetings progress and action items are completed, record meeting minutes on the standard meeting minutes form provided by the quality system manager. Each meeting attendee and this manager should receive one copy of the minutes, and, when necessary, an updated copy of the GANTT and control charts.

*11. Steps 4 through 10 should be considered iterative. That is, as solution attempts are made and improvement is or is not apparent, the plan and status of the plan should reflect new and continuous efforts to reduce the impact of the problem. This concept is the basis of a zero defects program. The ultimate goal of corrective action is to reduce the problem to an insignificant level by putting in place a program which *prevents* the problem from ever recurring. A second preventive action plan should, in most cases, not be written or implemented until the first action has been verified as having positive, negative, or no impact.

Zero defects and prevention are core concepts of the TQC/JIT.

12. There are one or two other concepts for the CAT to consider.

   A. Costs of quality – From a cost perspective, activities such as rework, inspection, test, returns, etc., are activities that, if the job were done correctly the first time, are added expenses which cause financial losses. The CAT should consider and make an effort to track and reduce such costs as part of their regular activities. The costs associated with administrative activities are difficult to track, but usually are significant contributors to manufacturing failures.

B. Costs of ownership – These costs usually refer to costs passed on to the customer of a particular activity or product. For example, a drawing error may cause inspection errors, drawing corrections, improperly manufactured product, and many other problems. Such associated costs are considered costs of ownership of the customer group.

C. Barriers to quality – A person trying her/his best to do a job correctly sometimes is restricted from accurate completion of the task. CATs should take some time to attempt to identify and list such barriers. Such lists should be passed up the chain of the organization to the TLT for action. Management has the responsibility to develop systems that eliminate barriers to quality.

D. Who is the customer? The customer is the next person to receive the output of your activities. Your customers vary depending on the particular activity you perform during the day. It is each CAT member's responsibility to understand and conform to their customers' requirements.

ESTABLISHING AND RUNNING FUNCTIONAL IMPROVEMENT TEAMS (FITS)

As mentioned in Chapter 1 the Functional Improvement Team is made up of members of a direct report group who all work together. This can be an accounting FIT, payroll FIT, production FIT, engineering FIT, customer services FIT, or any other group in the company. The FIT is the technique used to involve all personnel in the TQC/JIT system.

Generally, the FIT will meet at the same time in the same place once each week. It is at this time that the team selects a problem, establishes a method to measure the extent and trend of the problem, analyzes the problem to understand underlying causes, and plans and performs corrective action.

There always is a great deal of discussion regarding the establishment of FITs. Some companies and quality improvement teams decide to wait until FIT members are trained before establishing the team and allowing it to work. Other companies, which have found and hired strong in-house consulting support, have had great success encouraging and allowing FITs to form and begin prior to formal classroom training. Both strategies work.

Our preference is to establish teams, work with them until they understand their function, direction, and basic approaches, and then to let them go ahead until formal training is available. Naturally, this formal training must be planned and scheduled to ensure 100 percent coverage of employees. Formal training should take place within two to three months of team formation. Teams formed without formal training require occasional access to the internal or external consultant. The purpose of the consultant is to keep the FIT focused on the cycle of improvement, to settle disputes, and to provide in-meeting training as required.

Sooner or later the problem of scheduling FIT teams into limited meeting spaces will be encountered. To some extent, this can be overcome if FITs are meeting in their own work areas. On the other hand, a single meeting room, with proper scheduling and cooperation, can accommodate as many teams each week as there are hours in the work week.

There are some basic rules that apply to FIT meetings. Meetings should always begin and end on time. This requires and demonstrates commitment from all members. The meeting should be uninterrupted. Nothing destroys the perception of commitment faster than a boss running into a meeting and demanding to see a member! No interruptions for telephone calls should be allowed. Generally, people can live without coffee and cigarettes during this hour.

One uninterrupted hour per week means that one fortieth of the work week is allocated for a concentrated attack of quality problems. The manager or company that cannot support this meager effort should not begin a TQC/JIT effort.

The following section contains a set of guidelines for the operation of the FIT. Each member should receive one set of guidelines for reference purposes.

FUNCTIONAL IMPROVEMENT TEAM (FIT) GUIDELINES

The FIT is a functional improvement team meeting generally held at a regularly scheduled time each week. The purpose of an FIT is to identify and eliminate problems and quality barriers that cause defects which affect the overall department or section. Such problems or barriers are considered major or minor problems, and are generally caused and controlled by the individual department. Correction and future prevention, therefore, require a functional team effort.

All personnel are required to hold membership in at least one FIT. Typical functional improvement team agenda items include:

- Identifying unit-level problems that cause defects and excessive time cycles.
- Monitoring and reviewing defect tracking charts.
- Participatively setting short-term goals or objectives for defect or time-cycle reduction.
- Participatively planning actions to reach the objectives.
- Reviewing progress toward completion of action plans.
- Assigning corrective action responsibilities.
- Holding quality barrier discussions.
- Reviewing and updating defect logs.
- Providing training in problem-solving methods.

Each FIT will select a leader. The leader's responsibilities include:

• Schedule and hold FIT meetings.

• Ensure that all FIT members are trained in TQC/JIT strategies and techniques.

• Certify all FIT members to ensure their competencies in helping to implement TQC.

• Take a leadership role in discussions related to FIT functioning.

• Ensure that the FIT focuses on one clearly defined issue or problem at a time.

• Ensure that FIT meeting minutes are kept, reviewed, and forwarded to the TQC/JIT manager.

• Report the status of the FIT to the TQC/JIT manager.

• Forward important FIT issues, ideas, and concerns to higher-level FITs.

• Reward FIT members for their contributions.

• Keep the group on the road of continuous quality improvement.

FIT members have the following responsibilities:

• Attend and actively participate in all FIT meetings.

• Ensure that all action items are completed on time with quality performance and zero defects.

• Identify and report quality barriers.

• Identify and report quality costs.

• Maintain records which reflect FIT progress toward solving chosen TQC/JIT problems.

• Monitor all defect or other charts and take immediate corrective action on out of control conditions.

The general procedure for operation of the FIT is as follows. Techniques designed to support specific steps are presented in Chapter 4.

1. Select a meeting time and place.

2. Inform all functional personnel of the time, place, and purpose of the FIT meeting.

3. During the first meeting, review the elements of the TQC/JIT system, select a leader and a secretary to keep minutes and brainstorm problem areas. Record problems in meeting minutes. Introduce FIT members to standard report formats (GANTT chart [Chapter 3] for plans and control charts for tracking).

4. Clarify the major problem area for attack. Choose one part of the problem that can be solved in a reasonably short period of time (first round).

5. Determine a method for measuring the problem's current status. Begin data collection and chart the average reject rate (or time to complete [JIT] variable). This trend chart will later reflect the success or failure of each corrective action attempt. The chart will be presented to the TQT on a quarterly basis along with the GANTT chart described below (item 8).

6. Based on the current average, set a goal for improvement. This may be defect reduction, yield improvement, cycle time reduction, or any variable chosen.

7. Using standard Ishikawa diagramming methods, identify specific causal relationships and as a group, choose (plan) one problem solution attempt for the first round of corrective action. Analyze defects and rework loops which cause lost time.

8. Write the plan on a standard GANTT chart, and set activity objectives including the person responsible and the date due. The GANTT charted plan will be used to make presentations to the TQT along with the trend or control chart developed in step 5 above.

9. Begin the implementation of your plan and review and adjust the implementation during each weekly FIT meeting. Update the GANTT chart during each meeting.

10. As meetings progress and action items are completed, record meeting minutes on the standard meeting minutes form provided by the TQC/JIT manager. Each meeting attendee and the manager should receive one copy of the minutes and, when necessary, an updated copy of the GANTT and control charts.

*11. Steps 4 through 10 should be considered iterative. That is, as solution attempts are made and improvement is or is not apparent, the plan and status of the plan should reflect new and continuous efforts to reduce the impact of the problem. This concept is the basis of a zero defects program. The ultimate goal of corrective action is to reduce the problem to an insignificant level by putting in place a program that *prevents* the problem from ever recurring. A second preventive action plan should, in most cases, not be written or implemented until the first action has been verified as having positive, negative, or no impact.

Zero defects and prevention are core concepts of TQC/JIT.

12. There are one or two other concepts for the FIT to consider which are identical to CAT consideration.

A. Costs of quality – From a cost perspective, activities such as rework, inspection, test, returns, etc., are activities that, if the job were done correctly the first time, are added expenses which cause financial losses. The FIT should consider and make an effort to track and reduce such costs as part of their regular activities. The costs associated with administrative activities are difficult to track, but are usually significant contributors to manufacturing failures.

B. Costs of ownership – These costs usually refer to costs passed on to the customer of a particular activity or product. For example, a drawing error may cause inspection errors, drawing corrections, improperly manufactured product, and many other problems. Such associated costs are considered costs of ownership of the customer group.

C. Barriers to quality – A person trying her/his best to do a job correctly sometimes is restricted from accurate completion of the task. FITs should take some time to attempt to identify and list such barriers. Such lists should be passed up the chain of the organization to the TQT for action. Management has the responsibility to develop systems that eliminate barriers to quality.

D. Who is the customer? The customer is the next person to receive the output of your activities. Your customers vary depending on the particular activity you perform during the day. It is each FIT member's responsibility to understand and conform to their customers' requirements.

LEADERSHIP ISSUES

During the course of implementation of this TQC/JIT system at one U.S. company, the issue of *leadership* came up. Leaders of all CATs and FITs were collected into one room to list some things leaders should and should not do.

It was generally agreed that being an effective team leader was more difficult than had been previously anticipated. Many of the elected leaders were uncertain of how to handle various situations that came up in meetings. Table 2.5 summarizes their feelings about how to most effectively lead a team to success.

Table 2.5   What Team Leaders Should Do

1. Let *team members* set action items, plan, handle decision making and action items, and present ideas.

2. Listen carefully and accept ideas presented.

3. Be a leader, not a boss.

4. Provide a positive "we can" attitude.

5. Keep the group focused on the issues.

6. Encourage participation.

7. Provide recognition for good work.

8. Help prioritize.

9. Follow up on activity completion.

10. Assign or choose a backup leader.

    a. Meetings should be held even when the leader is absent.

    b. Leadership skills should be developed in all team members.

11. Interact with other TLT, FIT, and CAT leaders and members.

12. Leaders should *not* dominate discussions.

Table 2.5 lists some good ideas. If leadership problems arise in your company, this list may be used to help clarify issues with your staff, or it may be a good idea to hold a similar meeting and have team leaders define their own roles.

PROBLEMS INVOLVED WITH THE DELEGATION
OF AUTHORITY AND RESPONSIBILITY

As a quality professional, I had travelled to Korea for several years as part of my job. During that time, I saw many changes, not only in the companies, but in the country and people as well. Of course, the changes of the past few years have been most dramatic. The more traditional management styles of previous years are constantly being challenged, not only by students in the streets, but also by workers in the factories.

I have seen this same evolution take place in other countries. There is a good possibility that similar events will take place in Thailand and other developing countries over the next 10 years.

Interestingly, Korean professional quality publication articles have somewhat paralleled those in the United States. Articles dealing with TQC, employee participation, teamwork, and continuous improvement strategies are numerous in both countries. The articles in the United States, however, do not emphasize the same urgencies felt in Korea. In Korea, total quality systems are seen increasingly as a possible way of reuniting management and labor as corporate organizations attempt to regain stability after strikes. In the United States, strikes are not as frequent and TQC programs are "pushed" mainly by quality professionals constantly in search of quality improvement; sometimes pushed by top management and supported by other managers, but mostly endured until a slow agonizing death leaves yellowing SPC charts on the walls.

The answer to the question, Why is it so difficult to get management to joyously support companywide employee participation quality programs? may exist in many companies in many countries.

Corporate Culture

Whenever infighting, fingerpointing, frustration, employee turnover, and politics exist as the culture of the company, these are symptoms of lost control. The classic daily fire fighting agenda often results. Fifty to 75 percent of upper management's time may be spent in fire fighting, which means that time is taken away from the classic functions of management: staffing, planning, budgeting, organizing, and follow-through.[3] When upper management fails to distribute its time equitably among these functions, the organization fails to meet its goals. Lead times lengthen, systems are nonexistent, true preventive solutions are few and far between, expediting becomes the primary daily activity, and corrective action is rare.

The specific trail a company takes toward a state of chaos could be many and varied. A poor financial base, a corporate move or merger, authoritative leadership, top management turnover, rapid growth, or any of a number of catastrophic influences could set the beast in motion. After time, however, this chaos becomes the way of operating; much to the dissatisfaction of all involved. Unfortunately, it is during times of chaos that upper management clings to its perceived authority in futile attempts to control the company. At these times change is so rapid that any systematic control is lacking.

Organizational Culture Change

The truth is that management has and always will want people to take responsibility for solving problems. Unfortunately, authority usually is only granted as an employee moves upward in the hierarchy. In this manner, management maintains authority within its own ranks rather than through delegation.

The true meaning of cultural change within a company becomes apparent when authority and responsibility are delegated to lower levels as part of any employee involvement effort. When a total quality, statistical process control or just-in-time employee involvement program is launched, upper management's difficulties with control may be severely strained. Employees below the staff level begin to make decisions, take action, and change things. Staff level fear of losing control is likely to heighten. As staff members begin to hear how employees are changing things, staff begin to feel that their system and authority are being undermined.

True corporate or organizational cultural change has not

occurred until managers and employees are both comfortable with newly defined responsibility and authority structure. True cultural change has not occurred until the new management system has emerged.

Understanding the Change

As employees organize under a new facilitative team approach, rather than the more traditional directive method of management, they seize opportunities to identify, analyze, and control problems. This means that the quality system will be and is changing with less upper management need to "control" using the fire fighting, authoritarian, and directive strategies. When upper management begins to perceive such changes as being out of their control, defenses and insecurities may emerge. Management's role will change and the changes in their own roles are not within their control if they do not recognize, prepare for, and change with the new emerging system.

There is an important second side to this problem. Employees under a traditional system tend to expect direction rather than to set direction. Sometimes they are afraid to make changes without authority. This approval process sometimes can seem interminable and present bureaucratic barriers which force some employees to literally give up. Management is perceived as unable to make up its mind. Priorities change often and the reasons for those changes go uncommunicated to lower levels. The "they" concept emerges and a serious separation of upper and lower occurs tending to foster an atmosphere of distrust and disharmony. Long-term goals are not fulfilled and the company stalls in its effort to make headway in terms of growth, market share, and profitability.

The success of continuous improvement quality efforts depends on the abilities of top-level executives to understand and cope with a change in the organizational power structure. The authority to make many types of operational and system decisions historically has rested with those at the director or levels above. When continuous improvement is encouraged, by definition, authority must accompany responsibility to lower levels. With the implementation of any continuous-improvement, quality-oriented, employee-participation program, the emphasis on authority and responsibility delegation to lower levels has risen. Any employee-based continuous improvement effort that attempts to foster the acceptance of responsibility without concomitant delegation of authority is highly failure prone. While these programs proliferate, their actual impact is minimal and their lifetimes are of limited duration. True cultural change is never achieved.

The sharing of responsibility and authority is what many employees want. This is apparently why employees below the director level more quickly embrace and become involved in such programs while directors and those above that level may retreat into authoritarian postures during implementation. New leaders quickly emerge from the ranks furthering the perception of threat to higher-level managers. With reward systems in place, these new leaders earn public recognition while higher-level managers do not.

Management response often is a nonparticipative stance. The dissemination of negative comments about the lack of time or the waste of time, the relentless shifting of topics of discussion during quality improvement and JIT meetings, the domination of group discussions, the refusal to admit that problems listed by employees are truly problems, the verbalization of the "We can't do anything about that!" attitude rather than a positive "We can!" attitude, as well as many other barriers are presented to implementers. Farther down the line, as different improvement groups begin to discover each other and link up to reformulate corporate systems badly in need of review, threatened managers are capable of stonewalling changes by refusing to sign group-generated procedures and policies.

Under such circumstances, the continuous improvement effort begins to weaken, lose momentum, stall, and fade into the memory of those 15-year corporate veterans who "knew it wouldn't work" in the beginning.

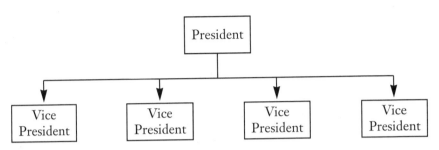

Figure 2.11   Top-Level Team

Some Solutions

Organization

Most solutions seem to lie within the structure and nature of the organization intended to implement and support the quality system. Figure 2.11 depicts a typical company with the top-level quality team consisting of vice presidents reporting directly to the president.

The issue of delegation of authority and responsibility must be openly discussed prior to any efforts to implement a continuous improvement employee involvement effort. Many top-quality consultants emphasize the need for top-level commitment without clearly identifying or discussing the true threat which looms on the horizon.

Commitment

This top-level commitment is operationalized by forming a top dog quality improvement team (QCT) whose members have the responsibility for planning and implementing the system. True commitment is easily observable during even the earliest stages of implementation. If the leader of the team (usually the company president) has to pound the table and threaten executive staff members to get action, commitment clearly is lacking. Generally, quality professionals say that the system must be *driven* into place by the top team. The need for such strong words reflects the true extent of resistance to change. The issues surrounding the reallocation of

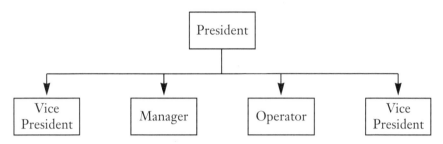

Figure 2.12   Top-Level Team

authority must be contemplated and planned for by any corporate implementation team.

In Korea, because of unions and strikes, top management often is forced to admit nonmanagement personnel to the top-level quality team (Figure 2.12). This is a strategy under test in Korea, but already successfully implemented by some American companies.

This strategy is the first and most serious true test of top-level commitment. If the top group will not share responsibility and authority for significant corporate decisions related to the implementation of the quality system, they will not be likely to later allow the system to foster an atmosphere of continuous improvement supported by all employees. The word "share" is critical. Executive staff members allowing nonmanagerial personnel to the quality team under the hammer of the president will quickly find ways to dump their responsibilities onto the nonmanagerial types while maintaining their authority, thereby sharing nothing.

Each member of the top quality team has one and only one vote. During all quality meetings, titles are left at the door. The room where meetings are held becomes a kind of sanctuary where no person holds a rank above another. All members have an equal right to present their views and alternatives to the group. Each member of the group has the responsibility to pay as much attention and give as much weight to the views of operators as would be given to the president.

It is often interesting to work with quality teams and observe other indicators of commitment. Many managers refuse to relinquish their perceived control of teams. In order for a system to become the new culture, managers must unselfishly help to develop in others the facilitative skills required to successfully implement continuous improvement. One problem frequently encountered is that managers themselves have not been trained to act as facilitators. The training of all managerial members must include facilitator training. Managers must, in turn, be content to pass on the responsibility of facilitator or leader and to continuously develop these skills in all team members.

As every group needs a leader, so too do all groups need to keep records of their progress. This duty of writing meeting minutes often falls on the shoulders of the lowest ranking person in the meeting. This is a sure sign of a lack of committed leadership and a symptom of the maintenance of authority at higher levels. All members of the team should take their turn handling tasks of this nature.

Respect

The need for an open, nonthreatening atmosphere where all members feel free to participate without ridicule or snide remarks surfacing at a later time is critical. All employee participation systems require that employees be encouraged to provide new insights and the group is expected to analyze problems, plan for and take corrective action. The manager must relinquish authority in such cases. The issue then becomes one of respect in the abilities of others to successfully solve problems. This means that if the group agrees to attempt a particular course of action, the manager may not override the group decision but has the responsibility to remove barriers to the group's success.

The manager should accept action items that require higher-level presentation, discussion, and decision-making in an effort to help the group solve the problem.

Leadership

The manager who sits in a quality meeting and dominates the group is not a leader, but is demonstrating serious insecurities resulting from a perceived loss of authority. The manager who, after a meeting in which an employee dared to disagree, takes the employee aside and ridicules or threatens the employee is also demonstrating a lack of leadership. There are several alternatives for dealing with this situation, because if such a lack of commitment is continually demonstrated, the participation system will not emerge.

Integrity

In every quality group formed, sooner or later the group and each member must deal with the issue of integrity. When any kind of action item is assigned or accepted, the member or subgroup must do everything possible to complete that assignment on schedule. The importance of individual integrity cannot be underemphasized. Nothing will make upper management step into and seemingly interfere with planned actions faster than the realization that group members are not fulfilling their agreed upon responsibilities to solve problems.

Patience

It is often said that a true continuous improvement employee-based system will take some years to implement. The truth is that if management could joyously accept and be prepared for the change in the decision-making process, the path to complete implementation would be significantly shorter. Since resistance to change generally exists anyway, resistance to the delegation of authority usually is excessive.

Continuous, patient, and unrelenting effort on the part of entrepreneurs is what makes businessmen successful. The same must be said for implementers of employee-based systems.

SUMMARY

The success of continuous improvement efforts depends on the abilities of top-level executives to understand and cope with a change in the organizational power structure. Although the authority to make many types of operational and system decisions has historically rested with those at higher organizational levels, when continuous improvement is encouraged, authority must accompany responsibility to lower levels.

With the attempted implementation of continuous-improvement, quality-oriented, employee-participation systems, the emphasis on authority and responsibility delegation to lower levels will rise. All efforts, such as JIT, TQC, and SPC, to foster the acceptance of responsibility without concomitant delegation of authority are likely to be expensive failures.

The struggles over authority and responsibility which may take place within the organization during the months and years it takes for such change efforts to succeed or die are many and varied. From the beginning, new perspectives, creative approaches, open-mindedness, and varied solutions to system problems must be attempted. Any continuous improvement system must itself be viewed as an organizational element in need of continuous improvement. The same tools applied in an effort to continually improve quality must be applied to the change system in an effort to continually improve it. This cycle includes identification of problems, monitoring, analysis of causes, and corrective action attempts.

In this chapter, the problem of conflicts resulting from changes and challenges to the distribution of responsibility and authority have been identified and explored.

Observations have been noted with which the reader may or may not identify. Causes have been discussed and corrective action has been recommended.

Implementation of a TQC/JIT system requires that an organizational structure of some sophistication be developed. This organization, consisting of a top-level team (TLT), functional improvement teams (FITs), and corrective action teams (CATs) help to collectively focus employees on change designed to enhance profitability. It is critical that the function of each team be clearly delineated. The top-level team is responsible for planning and managing the implementation of the TQC/JIT system. The functional improvement teams are responsible for identifying and solving problems within areas covered by their functional responsibilities. The corrective action teams are cross-functional groups established for purposes of attacking cross-functional problems, or for the purpose of performing some special JIT implementation activity, as described in Chapter 4.

Chapter 2 has described the specific responsibilities and activities of the top-level team. Chapters 3 and 4 intend to clarify the nonmanagerial, implementation activities for FITs, CATs, and special teams. Chapter 5 provides insight as to how different problems can be attacked from a cost-savings perspective.

3

System Implementation

FUNCTIONAL IMPROVEMENT TEAM (FIT) IMPLEMENTATION

*T*his chapter discusses the specific tools that corrective action teams (CATs) and functional improvement teams (FITs) use during team activities. Again, the top-level team (TLT) is responsible for system organization, policy setting, and the planning and management of activities presented in Table 2.1. CATs and FITs are responsible for team organization, the setting of priorities, developing and using some method of measuring the extent of problems, analysis of symptoms and causes, and taking improvement-oriented preventive action. The general outline of Table 1.3, item 4 is presented in more specific flowcharted detail as Figure 3.1.

This chapter will follow the outline presented as Figure 3.1.

Organizing the Team

The first team meeting will be called by the manager of the function or by the CAT leader chosen by the TLT. There are some concepts with regard to team formation that should be noted. In organizations

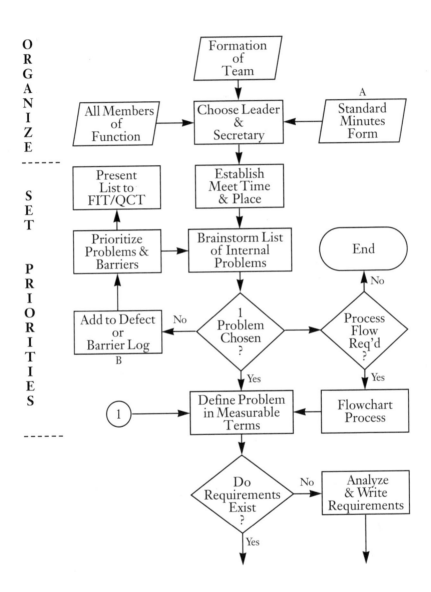

Figure 3.1

(Figure 3.1 continued)

(Figure 3.1 continued)

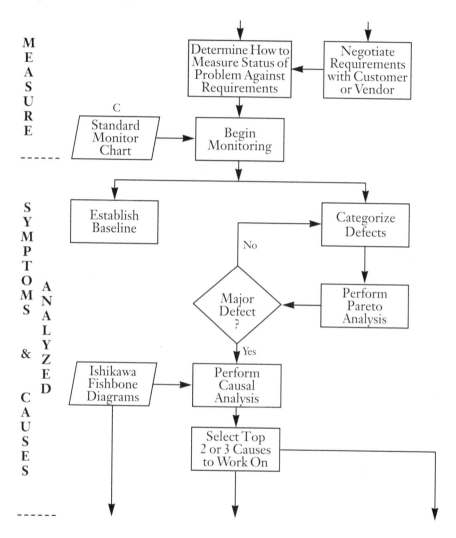

(Figure 3.1 continued)

(Figure 3.1 continued)

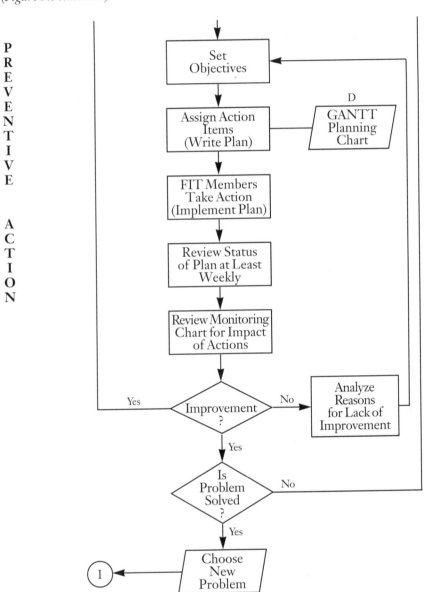

where teams are not a common daily mode of operation, the implementation of team corrective action attempts can cause some concern. Some teams seem to be able to choose a problem for focus and get up and running with no problem. Others take several meetings to truly identify and agree to the assigned task.

There are several reasons for the phenomenon of constantly being off-task. For instance, a leader with a strong personality can help or hinder a team depending on the person's style of leadership. Democratic leader types tend to do much better than authoritative leader types in TQC/JIT systems where authority and responsibility are to be delegated. Secondly, multiple strong personalities on the team often can detract from team effectiveness. Persons with strong personalities tend to vie with each other for the leadership position (regardless of the elected leader). A good deal of team meeting time can be lost while two opponents disagree on particular points. Another team problem occurs when no leader emerges. This leaves the team in a constant state of uncertainty about what to do next.

To control problems of strong and weak personalities, TLT members are advised to attend FIT and CAT meetings on a regular basis. The TLT member can help the team tremendously as an impartial observer with the role of gently but firmly moving discussions back on track. The team should remain focused on the particular point of work outlined below.

Another solution to the problem of off-task team discussions is to change leaders. Occasionally, an individual will be found who will not or cannot work as a team member. Consideration should be given to how the organization can avoid employing such personality types.

Choosing a Team Leader

The first function of the team is to select a leader. This is not always an easy task. The group manager should inform all members that anyone could become the team leader and that the leadership will rotate every two or three months. Nominations should be made and the vote can be secret or open, whichever the team chooses. The leader's functional role is described in Chapter 2 under the appropriate heading (CAT or FIT).

Choosing a Secretary

The second function of the team is to choose a secretary to record and forward minutes to the system manager for system summary purposes. The selection of the team secretary is generally met with a "Who, me?" attitude. No one seems to want this job, but the leader should assure all members that the job will be rotated every two months or so meaning that each member will have a turn as secretary. Usually this action results in a volunteer.

The secretary is given copies of the Standard Minutes Form on which to record minutes. There are proper and improper ways to record minutes. The Standard Minutes Form (Appendix D) is suggested here, but the system manager may substitute a different form if desired.

The Standard Minutes Form contains several sections which should be completed for each meeting held. The FIT/CAT name and date of meeting should be entered as well as the names of all attendees. The current meeting agenda item, discussion leader, and allotted time should be noted. Minutes and action items along with the person responsible for completion of the action item and the due date are recorded in the middle of the page. The minutes are then summarized, and the next meeting's agenda is recorded on the bottom of the sheet. A copy of this form should be forwarded to the system manager each week.

Within 24 hours, the secretary should distribute one copy to each team member. This is a critical time frame because occasionally a member will come to a meeting with an action item not completed ("I forgot"). Timely delivery of the meeting minutes helps people to remember their responsibilities. If the minutes are delivered the day before the next meeting, little time is left to complete action items.

Selecting a Meeting Time and Place

After the secretary is chosen and the minutes discussed, the team must choose a permanent time and place to meet. The meeting time and place should be frozen in concrete. All members should be expected to attend, on time, every week. No one, including the group leader or manager, should change this schedule once it is agreed upon. This may sound hard-line, but meetings will rarely take place if this suggestion is not followed.

Brainstorming

The purpose of the group should be clearly agreed upon. Remember that CATs already organized by the TLT have a defined problem, but the problem should be clarified and formally written for purposes of clearer communications. FITs have the task of choosing a problem that conforms to the three points in Table 3.1.

Table 3.1 FIT Team Problem Selection Criteria

1. Within team control.

2. Relatively easily solved.

3. Focused on cost reduction through time and quality improvements.

Recall that FITs are made up of members whose jobs are functionally related and who usually report to the same boss. Such functional cohesion suggests that the group members face similar problems on a daily basis. Some of these problems are repetitive, costly, and can be easily solved with TQC/JIT tools. Others are clearly interdepartmental in nature and require CAT action. The two types must be separated. Some problems are within the team control, but are relatively complex and will take a long time to solve. Complex problems are a legitimate team concern, but should be reserved until a later date when team members are familiar with team functioning and the use of system tools.

Table 3.2 represents a list of problems resulting from a brainstorming session held by a Purchasing FIT (example from the United States).

Table 3.2   Purchasing Department Problems (FIT List)

Bad vendors
Bad quality from vendors
No support from quality engineer
Phones too busy
Incorrect purchase requisitions
Office noise
Vendors with no appointments
Inaccurate MRP system
Vendor response time too long
Drawings out of revision
Poor payment of vendors
Other departments go around us
Lousy food in cafeteria
Vendor deliveries are late

Table 3.2 includes quite a variety of problems! Team leaders should not expect members to conform to the three rules listed in Table 3.1 during the first brainstorming session.

The initial team effort should attack a reasonably simple problem in order to ensure team success. This is an important motivational factor which should not be overlooked. New teams without TQC/JIT experience can become bogged down in complex problems which have long, drawn-out solutions. Complex problems should be avoided through the team's first problem-solving cycle. Such problems can be attacked at a later date when solutions will be quicker due to accumulated team experiences.

Using TQC/JIT tools to attack costly problems at any point in the organization is not necessarily an easy task. Most employees have no idea what costs are associated with different efforts. Many companies intentionally keep such information secret fearing the threat of disclosure to competitors. In other companies no internal means exists to determine such costs. Regardless, small groups can estimate costs using simple concepts presented in Chapter 4. There is no need for each group to lean on the financial department for exact-to-the-cent figures. Cost measurement should result in one general trend line which should react to successful system changes.

As an example, suppose the purchasing department, whose problems were listed in Table 3.2, decided to reduce staff-hours expended due to incorrectly completed purchase requisitions. Such staff-hours are easily logged. A standard burdened cost can then be assigned to the hours spent correcting errors, and by plotting such points each week, a trend line can be developed. The goal of the team would be to reduce the trend line through standard quality and time reduction efforts.

The brainstorming session which usually occurs during the first team meeting will result in many verbalized problems. Brain-storming is a simple technique designed to elicit numerous creative responses from a group. The leader can stand at a white board and write responses suggested by group members.

The rules of brainstorming are simple: No response is too ridiculous, all should be written down, and all members should participate. As many problems as possible should be identified and listed. Many responses will not meet the three criteria noted above, but all should be recorded anyway. Brainstorming this initial list usually takes 20 to 30 minutes and results in 10 to 50 items. Note that brainstorming will be inhibited if an authoritative boss is present who continually interferes with member ideas. Such bosses can be encouraged to miss a meeting or two until the team selects a problem.

The list should be copied by the secretary and distributed to all members as part of the meeting minutes. Most teams do not have time during the first meeting to reduce and prioritize the list. The one week interim between the first and second team meetings is a good time for team members to think about their problems and add to their personal lists.

Problem Selection

The second team meeting should open with a review of the initial list of problems, and members should be asked if they have anything to add. When no new items are added, the leader should remind members of the three rules previously listed. The list should then be reduced to only those items conforming to the rules. Discussion should be invited to help the team focus on one problem for attack. Most teams have no problem prioritizing the remaining problems and choosing one for the initial effort.

Occasionally, teams become confused and unfocused and are unable to agree on a single problem. A lack of focus and agreement will result for one of several reasons. Some teams are comprised of personnel with very different job functions. One solution is to break this team up into two separate, smaller teams. However, for purposes of solving the first problem, it usually is better to keep the team united. Members should understand, again, that even if the problem does not fall directly within their perceived area of responsibility or authority, solution of the problem is a team effort (100 percent involvement) and, for purposes of learning, the first problem attacked will give each smaller group the initial practical experience necessary to attack and solve subsequent problems.

Another common reason for the team to be unable to choose one problem is that the functional boss may be interfering with team functioning. If the functional boss does not want the team to work on, or does not admit to a particular problem, the team will have a difficult time getting underway. Members may choose not to contribute to the group discussions because they are politically astute enough to realize the boss will get even somehow. This is a particularly difficult situation because the boss is accustomed to being the boss, and as such, running the show. Some functional bosses are threatened by the elected leader and respond through political maneuvering (see Chapter 2's discussion on "Delegation of Authority and Responsibility"). TQC/JIT teams are without bosses but require a new type of leadership. In some cases, it has been necessary to appeal to higher authorities to help the boss understand the changing system.

Again, most teams do not run into difficulty through the brainstorming and problem selection exercises.

Defining the Process Flow

The team's usual next task is to flowchart the process involved. Whether the process is an administrative or manufacturing problem makes no difference when flowcharts are developed. There are several useful symbols which are used to develop simple flowcharts. These are illustrated in Figure 3.2.

Figure 3.1 can be used to illustrate the use of these symbols to clearly define a process. The parallelogram is used to indicate input or output, beginning or end. The rectangle is used to show process steps or activities. The diamond is used for decision points, and circles are used to illustrate how various steps connect together without cluttering the flowchart with too many crisscrossing lines.

Some basic assumptions should guide the development and use of process flowcharts (Table 3.3).

Table 3.3   Flowcharting Assumptions

1. All jobs are part of a sequence of activities which can be defined in writing.

2. Knowledge of the sequence of steps in the job flow can help one understand the job and identify potential bottlenecks and problem areas.

3. Flowchart symbols can be used to illustrate the sequence of inputs, activities, decisions, and outputs.

4. Flowcharts show interrelationships among job steps better than written job descriptions.

5. Flowcharts make job flows and procedures easier to understand than written versions, but users must be trained in their use.

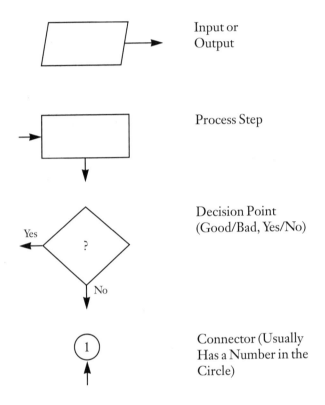

Input or
Output

Process Step

Decision Point
(Good/Bad, Yes/No)

Connector (Usually
Has a Number in the
Circle)

Figure 3.2   Process Flowchart Symbols

The last point is particularly important. Many companies use flowcharts but never train employees in their use. This is a mistake!

Figure 3.3 is a sample flowchart developed to illustrate a data checking and keypunching operation. (Yes! Some organizations still use keypunch machines.) Data are received (input symbol), counted and screened for errors (process step symbol), and separated (decision symbol, if error, then return to manufacturing; if no error, go to keypunch), keypunch checks for errors again (decision symbol; a different type of error) and returns (process symbol) or keypunches (process symbol) after which forms are filed for two months (process symbol) then discarded (output symbol). Two error checks means two inspection steps. A likely spot for step elimination in a JIT environment.

Once the FIT team has chosen and carefully defined the problem, the next critical step is to determine whether or not requirements currently exist that will help measure the timeliness or quality of the situation. Returning to the purchasing dilemma, the purchasing FIT found that no procedures, explanations, or requirements had been written to guide those desiring to complete purchase requisitions. Furthermore, a review of the purchase requisition itself revealed that the form was confusing and difficult to complete. Indeed, members of the purchasing FIT disagreed on the correct manner for form completion. At this point, it became clear to FIT members why they spent so much time and effort trying to get completed forms reworked so that accurate orders could be placed. Corrective action strategies were already forming in their minds.

If quality means "meeting the requirements" and no requirements exist, then quality cannot be measured. There is simply no standard against which to compare the real world to the ideal world.

As for how long it should take to process and disposition a purchase requisition, no one knew how long it took on the average, and no target had been established.

This is an interesting and typical case. Most departments tend to blame other departments for problems. It is the rare manager who

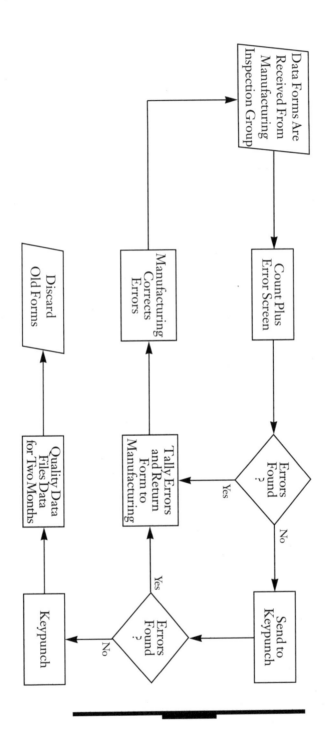

Figure 3.3   Sample Flowchart

identifies and claims responsibility for solving seemingly external problems. Such actions are dangerous in most companies because the other department manager undoubtedly will feel stepped on. Negative reactions are generally predictable, but may be overcome if the other department manager is convinced that his or her department is perceived as the customer.

For the purchasing group, they had historically, for several years, blamed everyone else in the company for incorrectly filling out purchase requisitions. As a result of their involvement with the TQC/JIT system, they began to identify and take responsibility for problems they and the rest of the company had lived with for some time. No one knows how much time and money was spent reworking incorrect purchase requisitions through that time. They began to perceive themselves as a vendor with a customer base to serve. Quite a change.

One critical aspect to the development of requirements and procedures is that the defined customer, and, indeed, identified vendors, must be involved in the development of the requirements. Such instances demand that a representative of the involved FITs meet to discuss the problem and organize to help each other. Support usually is easily generated if one member of the FIT will visit the customer and vendor FIT meetings and discuss the problem with the entire team. Not only does this foster goodwill between previously opposing departments, but problems begin to be perceived as mutual resulting in sharing of cooperation and solution.

Measurement and Data Presentation

Once requirements are written and agreed on by the FIT and its customers and vendors, the team must determine how to measure the extent of the problem. Measurement means that a method to collect and report data must be developed.

Most team members have successfully avoided statistics courses during their college careers. If such courses could not be avoided, they certainly were dreaded. Once initial fears are overcome, data collection, analysis, and presentation become a standard way of life.

The prospect of figuring out how to measure previously unmeasured items of interest can be stressful. Once the team overcomes the trauma of the first attempt, subsequent data collection efforts are much easier.

Returning to the example of the purchasing department, the FIT decided to measure the number of rejected purchase requisitions they received. Armed with the agreed upon requirements, the team set up a subcommittee to inspect the incoming purchase requisitions. The result was a tally of defects matched to specific requirements. After reviewing 25 purchase requisitions, it was found that all (100 percent) had at least one error, most had two or three. After three weeks of similar analysis, the FIT found that the 100 percent finding continued. When inspected against the requirements, no purchase requisition went through without some rework, phone call, or rejection back to the issuing department. At this point the team decided to track department staff-hours expended to correct purchase requisitions. The intent was to convert the staff-hours to standard burdened labor costs and design corrective action to reduce these costs.

The most informative and simplest method of presenting data is in the form of a trend line. In more sophisticated forms, the trend line becomes a control chart. Control charts often are used as tools in statistical process control (SPC) subsystems. Figure 3.4 shows a trend line which began as an out of control condition with great variability (A). The condition was improved and brought under control (less variability) through initial corrective action (B), and, eventually, greatly improved with further successful corrective actions (C). Whether the chart reflects costs, defect levels, or time in process is not indicated in this example. The important point is that the trend shows improvement from an uncontrolled high problem state to a controlled low-level problem state. The trend is highly visible and easy for anyone to interpret.

Some teams choose to present results using bar charts, often in creative form. If bar charts are used, the chart should not attempt to

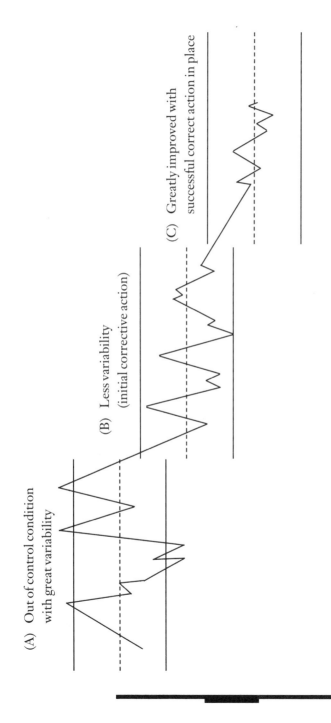

Figure 3.4 Trend Line

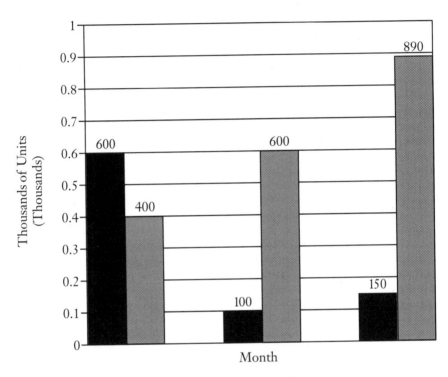

Figure 3.5   ARM JIT Improvements: Top Assembly

illustrate too many (no more than two) variables at one time. Any chart that attempts to show three or four (or more) variables becomes confusing and difficult to interpret. Figure 3.5 is a bar chart showing ending inventory and production trends as a result of implementing TQC/JIT strategies in a production line. Both trends are favorable. Inventory in the line at the end of the shift dropped from a daily average of 600 parts in March to 100 to 150 parts per day in April and May. There is still plenty of room for improvement, probably through the use of KANBANs with reduced lot sizes. Production also shows great improvement, from 400 finished parts per day to 890 per day over the three-month period. This is a clean chart which communicates results clearly.

Some general recommendations for data presentation are presented in Table 3.4.

Table 3.4   Recommendations for Presenting Data

1. Data should be plotted to clearly show the trend and communicate the status of the problem.

2. The Y (vertical) axis of the plot should be used for counts, percents, dollars, etc., and should show the level of the variable (e.g., percent of defective forms, time expended for rework, dollars lost on scrap).

3. The X (horizontal) axis of the plot is always used to show time (days, weeks, months, years).

4. The longer the time line, the clearer the trend will become. Do not chop off charts showing only short trends. If too many points clutter the chart, turn the daily points into weekly averages, turn the weekly points into monthly averages, etc.

5. No more than two variables should be shown on any one chart.

6. The Y axis should range from a low point to a high point in a manner that does not exclude plotted points above or below the chart's capabilities and in a manner that does not intentionally visually distort the chart to make trends appear favorable when the reverse is true.

7. The chart should have a title. X and Y axes should be labeled. Clearly labeled supporting data may be presented at the bottom of the chart.

Figure 3.6 is an example that violates many of the suggestions presented in Table 3.4. Confusion is unacceptable.

The purchasing department plotted two charts. The percent of purchase requisitions rejected on a weekly basis resulted in a chart

ECR/ECO QTY'S AND REASONS FOR ----------

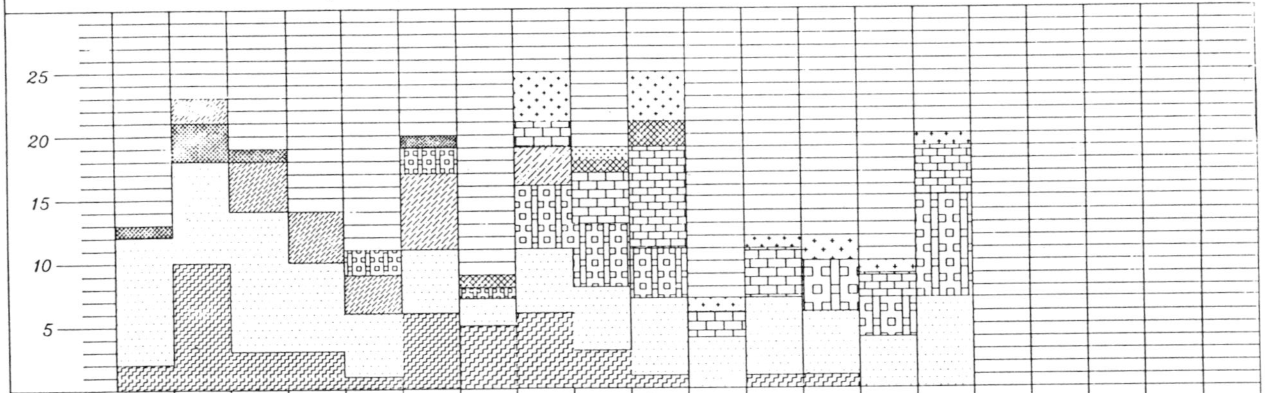

DATE	2/1-5	2/8-12	2/15-19	2/22-26	2/29-3/4	3/7-11	3/14-18	3/21-25	3/28-4/1	4/4-4/8	4/11-15	4/18-22	4/25-29	5/2-6	5/2-13
IC	1	3	1		1	1	1	3	1	2					
IP		2	4	7											
N	10	8	11		5	5	2	5	5	6	3	6	5	4	7
O				4	3	6	1	2	4	8	1	4	2	1	1
P					2	2		4	1	4	2	1	4	2	4
C							5	5	5	4		1	1	3	8
E	2	10	3	3		6		6	3	1					
TOTAL	13	23	19	14	11	20	9	25	19	25	6	12	12	10	20

REMARK:

O = OTHER
IC = CUSTOMER DICTATED CHANGE INITIATED
IP = MFG PROCESS CHANGE, VENDOR REQUEST, COST REDUCTION, INITIATED
N = NEW RELEASE OF DOCUMENT
S = CUSTOMER SPEC RECEIPT, NO DOC CHANGE REQUIRED
P = MFG PROCESS CHANGE, VENDOR REQUEST, COST REDUCTION
C = CUSTOMER DICTATED CHANGE (VENDOR AND CUSTOMER DWGS)
E = ERROR BY (VENDOR AND CUSTOMER DWGS)

Figure 3.6   An Unacceptable Chart

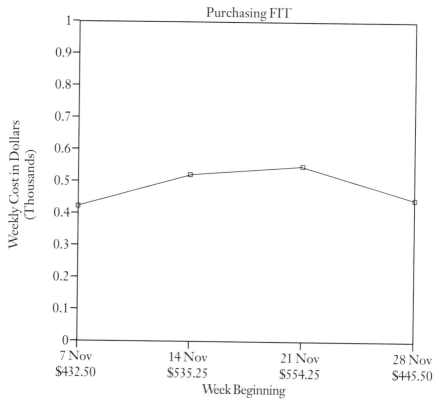

Figure 3.7   Cost of PR Rework

that, for three consecutive weeks, showed 100 percent rejection. This is a straight line across the top of a chart. The second chart plotted was a cost chart. Based on the assumption that a buyer was worth $30.15 per hour (including overhead) and a clerk was worth $17.50 per hour, the resulting data and chart appeared as in Figure 3.7. Figure 3.7 is a good example of a standard monitoring chart (Figure 3.1, item C).

If a straight line is drawn through the points, an average of $491.90 was being spent each week to track down and correct purchase requisition errors. This amounts to $25,578 ($491.9 x 52 weeks) wasted each year! Add this to the fact that purchase requisitions were delayed by all the rework and you have a classic TQC/JIT problem.

The purchasing FIT had now identified a problem, clarified requirements, and begun monitoring. The $491.90 may be considered a baseline figure. This number is used to set objectives for improvement. The obvious objective is to reduce the average dollar losses. This can be accomplished by determining specific causes for defects and setting preventive action plans and actions to change the current system to prevent such defects from recurring.

Categorizing Defects

Categorizing defects means to establish classifications of defects, tally the occurrence of defects into their respective categories, and set up an analysis to visually reveal the most frequently occurring defects (or costs, lost time or other variable). This process is called Pareto analysis.

A Pareto analysis of purchase order defects is completed in the following manner. A classification system for defects must be established. This is commonly done in manufacturing. Most quality inspectors and quality engineers are familiar with Pareto analysis.

In our example, the purchasing FIT, using the requirements for acceptable purchase requisitions, inspected each purchase requisition for nonconformance to the requirements. Table 3.5 shows the results of their study for a one-week period.

Cost Analysis

Costs, in this case, were analyzed by determining the standard burdened labor rate for a buyer ($30.50 per hour) and a clerk ($17.50 per hour). These amounts were multiplied times the number of hours worked to correct mistakes, audit purchase requisitions, and record information to arrive at a per person cost each week (Table 3.5, bottom). Added together, the total weekly cost was estimated to be $535.25. If similar data are collected for a period of several weeks,

Table 3.5 Purchase Order Defects
(Date of Report: Nov. 14 – 18, 1988)

P	Defect Name	Number of Defects Which Occurred
6	No quantity noted	2
1	No approval signature	25
3	Price of purchase missing	11
5	No delivery location noted	3
2	No recommended vendor	14
4	Requesting person unknown	6
7	Requested delivery date missing	1
6	Capital asset item with no approved budget	2

Total number of purchase requisitions reviewed = 25
Total number of purchase requisitions rejected = 25
Percent of reject = 100%   Percent of Acceptance = 0%
Total number of defects = 64
Average defects per purchase requisition (64/25) = 2.56

Purchasing staff-hours expended: Buyer 5.5 @ $30.50 = $167.75
Clerk 21.0 @ $17.50 = $367.50
Total staff-hour rework cost = $535.25

an estimated average weekly cost can be calculated easily (see analysis below).

Pareto Analysis

This data was collected weekly. For purposes of illustration, data from Table 3.5 are presented in the form of a Pareto analysis. In fact, data from all four weeks could be used to set up the Pareto analysis. Larger data bases generally give a more accurate picture of defect occurrences.

To set up a Pareto is quite simple. To begin with, the data in the

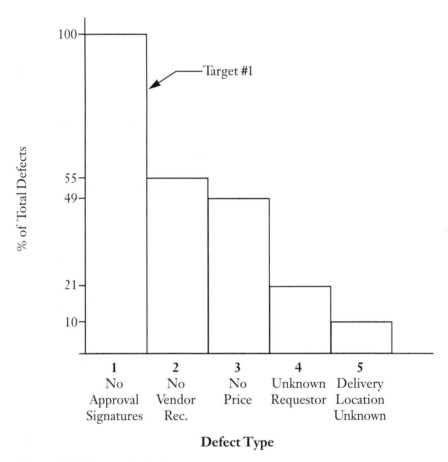

Figure 3.8   Pareto Analysis

table must be rearranged according to the frequency of occurrence. In other cases frequency of occurrence figures might represent lost time, wasted dollars, percent of defects, number of defects, or any of many different variables. The point is that although Pareto analyses are most frequently seen depicting defects, they can be used to represent almost anything quantifiable. The purpose is to quantify and visually separate the large problems from the small ones. The number one problem has the largest line on the chart and this usually is

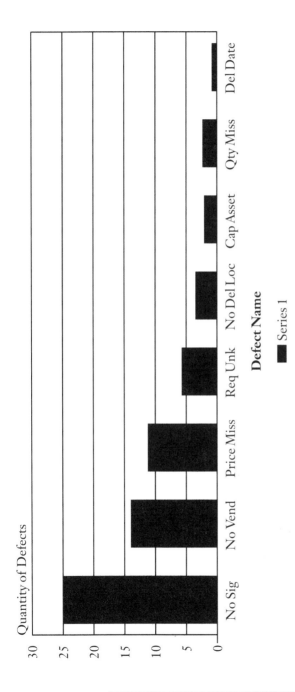

Figure 3.9 Purchase Order Pareto Analysis (November 14 – 18, 1988)

the number one target for correction (Figure 3.8).

The column labeled "P" in Table 3.5 shows the priority of each defect type. The data indicate that no requisition contained an approval signature. All 25 requisitions could have been rejected on this basis alone since the requirements stated that all purchase requisitions must be approved.

The remainder of the priorities were assigned in the same way, according to the number of occurrences of each type. This data was then visually depicted as shown in Figure 3.9. This figure is commonly known as a Pareto analysis. The analysis made it clear where the most impact could be made. If the team could ensure that all (100 percent) purchase requisitions submitted to the purchasing department contain approval signatures, they would have significantly reduced the reject rate, associated rework rates, and delays in purchase requisition processing. Causal analysis and corrective action strategies are discussed below.

Cycle-Time Analysis

Pareto analysis is used primarily with regard to frequency or costs of defects, but another important visual analytical tool focuses on cycle times. Cycle time analysis is a specialized type of Pareto analysis which focuses on time factors.

Cycle time is considered a critical variable of interest to JIT implementation. In its simplest form, cycle time refers to the time period material takes to go from the beginning of a manufacturing line to the end of that line. In many companies where JIT is implemented from the vendor to the customer, cycle time is calculated from the time materials arrive at the receiving dock until final product is deposited on the customer's receiving dock.

The theory is that a large volume of material (large lot sizes) will require a longer time to go through manufacturing than a small lot. Cycle time analysis reveals how long the material is at each operation and how long material sits and waits between or in operations. JIT uses cycle time to drive the lot size down so the in-line inventory and time in work-in-process (WIP) or time-in-plant are minimal. The effect of controlling material volume and cycle time is that less inventory is required to keep manufacturing at full production. Less inventory means that fewer dollars need to be spent and the time money is tied up in inventory is greatly reduced. If less money is required to supply a full production facility with materials and the materials are converted into finished goods in less time, the money used to buy materials can be used more often each year as sales of finished products is speeded up. This improves what is known as *inventory turns*.

For example, most electronics companies show inventory turns at about three to four times each year.[14] Money used to buy materials is converted into finished product, thus into sales (and hopefully profit) dollars. The more times a company turns the inventory from raw materials into finished product, the higher the profit margin.

If a company invests $1,000 in inventory and sells the finished product for $2,000, the difference is $1,000. If the company does the same thing four times a year, the same $1,000 can be used four times to give the company the difference between cost and sales price four times – $4,000. If the same company has 25 inventory turns each year, the same $1,000 investment is reused 25 times which grosses the company $25,000 each year. There is a lot of difference between $4,000 and $25,000, thus the drive to improve inventory turns.

Inventory turns can be calculated from any company's balance sheet and consolidated income statement. The balance sheet reports the dollar value of inventories at year's end.[1] All companies involved in manufacturing try to reduce this number as far as possible, especially at the end of the fiscal year. That is part of the reason why employees in manufacturing feel such huge pressure to ship as much as possible at the end of the fiscal year. This annual effort to reduce inventories is also one of the greatest threats to TQC attitudes and practices.

The consolidated income statement has a second important number. This is the *net sales* number.[1] The net sales figure is used in a variety of financial calculations, but for purposes of calculating inventory turns, this number is divided by the inventory number and the result is the number of times a company turned its inventory throughout the year. As an example, a company with $11,000,000 in sales ended up with $2,700,000 worth of inventory on December 31. Dividing $11,000,000 by $2,700,000 gives 4.1 as the inventory turns.

Some Japanese companies report more than 125 inventory turns each year. It is no wonder they are able to show greater profitability than many other manufacturing countries. The Japanese have had great success controlling through-the-plant cycle times using TQC/JIT strategies.

The concept of cycle time and the rewards to be reaped from controlling cycle times does not end with manufacturing. The purchasing group used throughout this chapter could have just as easily chosen to focus on delays in filling purchase orders and used defect and cost targets as secondary analyses. It is no secret that paperwork bottlenecks cause significant delays not only in purchasing of materials and equipment, but in response time to external customer inquiries and quotes, computer input, payroll, document control, engineering, and other areas. Cycle analysis for paper flow processes is identical to that used in manufacturing in the same manner that other TQC/JIT tools are useful in all areas of the company.

Cycle analysis is easy to implement. In manufacturing, a single part or small lot can be tagged or color-coded when it enters the line. A traveller is attached to allow each operation to record the time into and out of the operation. Figure 3.10 shows such a traveller.

Figure 3.10 shows seven operations, from winding through packing. The date, lot number, lot size, and time in and out of each operation and cumulative times were recorded on the form. The elapsed times were then calculated. The difference, in minutes, between the time in and the time out gives the elapsed minutes for each operation. This represents how long the lot stayed in the operation. Notice, however, that the materials were signed out of the winding operation at 11:30 but were not signed into bonding until

Date: 15 Feb. 1988		Lot Number: K1203A		Lot Size = 100
Operation	Time In	Time Out	Elapsed Mins	Cum
Winding	08:00	11:30	210	210
		Wait =	30	240
Bonding	12:00	13:00	60	300
		Wait =	15	315
Oven cure	13:15	15:25	130	445
		Wait =	30	475
X - Y check	15:55	16:20	25	500
		Wait =	25	525
Route/crimp	16:45	17:45	60	585
		Wait =	160	745
Inspection	20:25	21:00	35	780
		Wait =	0	780
Packing	21:00	21:25	25	805
		Total WIP Time =		805 Mins
		(805/60 = 13.42)		13.42 Hours

Figure 3.10　Cycle Time Record Sheet

12:00. This represents 30 minutes of time the materials spent waiting on the line. This is shown as the "Wait" time between winding and bonding.

The remainder of the elapsed times are calculated similarly, accumulated in the last column and totaled to show the "Total WIP Time" at the bottom of the form. By adding each elapsed time to the subtotal in the "Cum" column, a running total can be calculated. The cumulative total is used in the next stage of cycle time analysis.

In all, the materials were in WIP for 13.42 hours (805 minutes). Considering the fact that the accumulation of time it actually takes to complete all operations is about 20 minutes, the difference between 805 and 20 is substantial. The 785-minute difference is JIT's target.

Theoretically, if each part was passed through the line with each operation working at standard speed and with no (or minimum) wait time between operations, the materials would flow like a river.

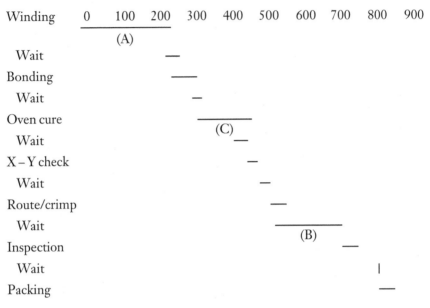

Figure 3.11   Cycle-Time Analysis Chart

Remember in Chapter 1 that it was suggested that materials and paperwork be viewed as moving, not as static. Material slugging through a line in 13.42 hours can hardly be considered flowing. The line is obviously out of balance and probably glutted with materials, quality problems, too many operations, too much handling, and certainly too much waiting.

Data from Figure 3.10 are presented in Figure 3.11 to graphically illustrate the relationships between process and wait times, and between process and process times. Figure 3.11 is a visual display of data shown in Figure 3.10. Across the top of the chart is a running clock from zero to 900 minutes. Data from the "Cum" column in Figure 3.10 are depicted on this chart. For instance, winding took 210 minutes. The winding line runs from zero to 210 and is followed by a wait line of 30 minutes.

By graphing the data in this manner, the parts of the process which take the most time are highlighted. Lines A, B, and C stand out as the three top contenders for corrective action in much the same way that the Pareto analysis (Figure 3.9) visually depicted the defect priorities. Winding, the wait time between route/crimp and inspection, and oven cure are major contributors to the overall 805-minute cycle time. Obviously, there are imbalances in the manufacturing line which may become the priority for a FIT or CAT team. These imbalances can be corrected by the team using Chapter 1 concepts and the ideas presented below.

In the event that a team is assigned or chooses to work on a time reduction (JIT) problem, the team can use the analyses in Figures 3.10 and 3.11 to monitor the overall cycle time trend. This is simply done by collecting and analyzing data on at least a weekly basis and plotting either the total through-the-line hours or minutes calculated at the bottom of Figure 3.10. By plotting the cycle time found in successive weeks, a trend line will develop. The average cycle time may be calculated by adding the total minute times together from several weeks and then by dividing the resulting total by the number of weeks used in the analysis. If the average cycle time is drawn on the chart as a straight line, the base line is thereby established and the team can set objectives for cycle-time reduction. Causes for the excessive operation or wait times may be analyzed using the causal analysis methods which follow. Preventive action may be planned and implemented, also using standard approaches as described. Focusing actions on the easiest-to-fix time periods is the quickest way to achieve cycle-time reduction results. In the case presented, the wait time between route/crimp and inspection probably is a quick fix.

Any team working on cycle-time reductions must be aware of one rule. No negative impact to quality can be allowed. In other words, corrective or preventive actions which cause quality problems are bound to result in disaster. Product or process quality levels must be monitored to ensure that this does not occur.

In manufacturing, cycle-time reductions generally result from reduction of lot sizes. However, lot-size reduction requires careful study and planning. Lines often have to be rebalanced, have new floor layouts, and sometimes require additional equipment. Despite these drawbacks, lot-size reduction has such powerful impact that vast savings in floor space, yield improvements, material handling, cost of production, and cost of inventory result.

Causal Analysis

The next question to be asked in any situation where a Pareto or cycle time analysis has clearly given an indication of the most frequently occurring defect or time problem is, "What is the cause?"[9] This is a case where a tool known as the *fishbone diagram* or cause-and-effect diagrams are used (Ishikawa). Cause-and-effect diagrams are used widely throughout quality programs. Their application has been primarily in manufacturing environments where defects have been identified, and individuals or groups have wished to brainstorm to note possible causes. The tool is equally valuable to nonmanufacturing problems.

Any time causal analysis is begun, care must be taken to intelligently link series of potential causes together in a logical manner. For instance, suppose the electricity went off in your building right now. You would think of many possible causes. First, you might think someone turned off the power intentionally although why they might have done so might escape you. On the other hand, there could be a power outage in your area of the town, or even throughout the entire city. This, in turn, could be caused by a number of factors. Perhaps a main generator has failed or a truck crashed into a power pole. Perhaps World War III has started. No, probably a circuit breaker went off due to some power overload, but no new equipment has been purchased, so no new power requirements were established.

Suppose a circuit breaker did cut off the power. Why did it do so? Did the circuit breaker fail or did it actually do the job it was designed to do? If it failed, was it incorrectly installed? Was the wrong one installed? or Was it manufactured as a defective unit? If it was incorrectly installed, who installed it? Were they trained?

• Tooling and equipment do not meet CPk > 1.33.

• Materials used to build do not meet spec.

• People – not properly trained or make mistakes.

• Methods for the process are not clear or accurate.

• Measurement methods are incorrect.

• The environment will not properly support the manufacturing requirements.

(Main categories)

Figure 3.12   Manufacturing Cause-and-Effect

Did they have the proper tools? Was the wiring diagram correct? The inquiry could go on for some time as each possible cause is investigated until, hopefully, the true cause will be found and corrected to the extent that it will be prevented in the future. Usually, the cause for power failures is quickly detected and eliminated. This is not always the case when dealing in an administrative or manufacturing environment.

The purchasing FIT certainly had a question to answer. Their analysis showed that 100 percent of the purchase requisitions coming into their department did not have appropriate approval signatures. They had many hypotheses. They decided to use the cause-and-effect diagram to guide their efforts.

Chapter 1, Figure 1.1 is a simple illustration of a cause-and-effect diagram. Quality was perceived as the result of every person in every department. The illustration is far from complete since there could be causes of causes, of causes, etc.

In order to develop and expand a cause-and-effect diagram, the FIT usually engages in a lot of brainstorming. The relationships that may be shown on a cause-and-effect diagram are significant. The series of "Why?" questions that may be asked are lengthy.

In manufacturing, where problems and causes are varied, FIT and CAT teams should consider several main categories to begin the diagram. Figure 3.12 shows these categories. Tooling that was not designed, built, nor maintained to hold adequate process capabilities must be considered as a main source of quality or time problems. Materials that do not meet specifications may be received, and due to production pressures, "bought off" and put into the line where multiple problems can arise. People may not be properly trained, or may be rushed to get the job done. Often, process procedures or specifications are out of revision, contain mistakes, or may even be for the wrong product. Inspection personnel may reject perfectly good product or fail to reject product which does not meet customer requirements due to improper inspection methods, specifications, or equipment. In some circumstances, the facility itself may be to blame. A product that requires a clean environment may be rejected because the air conditioning system cannot filter the air properly. Or, the lighting may be too poor for operators to adequately see the work.

These main categories are used to begin production team discussions focused on production problems. The cause-and-effect diagram to begin such an investigation will look like Figure 3.13.

Returning to the purchasing FIT and the results of the Pareto analysis they performed, recall that the number one reason for rejected purchase requisitions was that they contained no signatures. Number two was that no vendor was recommended. Number three was that the purchase price was not included on the form. The beginning cause-and-effect diagram for this problem is shown as Figure 3.14.

Beginning with the number one defect of "no signature," the team was asked why there was no signature on the forms. They felt that no procedure had been established. When asked why not, the response was that none had been written. Again, "Why not?" The response this time was that it was not required. Other suggested possible causes for no signature phenomenon included "People don't know (it is required)," and the "Boss (was) absent."

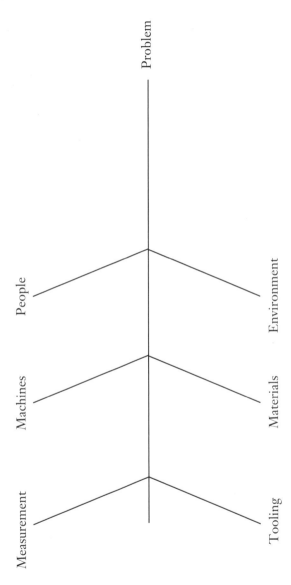

Figure 3.13   Basic Cause-and-Effect

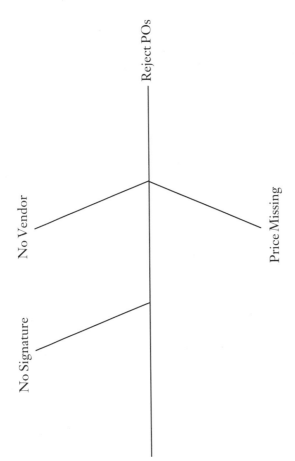

Reject POs

No Vendor

Price Missing

No Signature

Figure 3.14 Purchasing Analysis

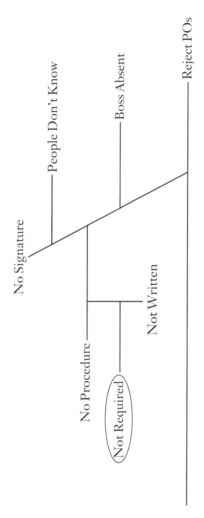

Figure 3.15 No Signature Analysis

Statement of Problem:

Name of CAT/FIT		TQC/JIT Improvement System					
Leader/Members		Implementation Action Items and Corrective Action Plan					
Activity	Person Respons	Feb 1 2 3 4	March 1 2 3 4	April 1 2 3 4	May 1 2 3 4	June 1 2 3 4	July 1 2 3 4

Figure 3.16   GANTT Chart

Aug 1 2 3 4	Sept 1 2 3 4	Oct 1 2 3 4	Nov 1 2 3 4	Dec 1 2 3 4	Jan 1 2 3 4	Status of Activity

Selecting the Top Cause(s)

The team was asked what they thought was the most likely cause. The response was that signatures had not been required. The analysis is shown as Figure 3.15.

In this case, the team had, through a series of simple analyses and tools, pointed themselves in the direction of a clearer and more likely successful preventive action.

The purchasing FIT case is a simple example of how to collect and analyze data in order to focus corrective action attempts. Not all problems are so simple. Indeed, when this team started their FIT activities with a brainstorming activity to list their internal problems, they had no idea that the answer had been there all along. Historically, they had simply spent much of their time reworking the incorrect purchase requisitions while blaming everyone else in the company for the problem. With the resulting bottlenecks in the purchasing department, their boss hired extra people to help with the work load. The cost of nonquality was very high when multiplied by every department in the company.

In the team's early TQC/JIT attempts they had discovered, as is often the case, that requirements did not even exist for them to separate good quality (meeting the requirements) purchase requisitions from poor quality requisitions. By developing such requirements, they had begun the job of preventing such problems from recurring.

Corrective Action

Recall that the term *corrective action* means *preventive action*.

Using the GANTT planning chart depicted in Figure 3.16, the team is ready to establish a plan for correcting the problem. The exact form of the chart is not critical.

Basically, the chart includes a calendar across the top and spaces for writing action items down the left-hand column. Some teams choose to show days of weeks in the calendar section rather than weeks of months. This decision depends on the duration of planned corrective action. The target date for completion of each action item is marked with an X or some other symbol in the column under the appropriate date. The second column is used to record the name or names of team members responsible for completion of the action item. The far-right-hand column allows the team leader to record information or problems relative to the status of implementation of each activity.

Although the chart's main purpose is to provide a team planning format, information recorded on the chart is used to track implementation status. Action items may be completed either ahead of time or later. Early and late completions should be recorded on the chart for use in determining individual accountability. This chart also is used to communicate the plan and activity status to other teams.

Team discussions directed at determining which action items should be attempted to correct problems should be open and creative. The word "creative" is critical here. Often the best solutions to problems are the simplest ones. Basic TQC/JIT concepts presented in Chapter 1 should be reviewed to ensure that these concepts are operationalized in each plan. The team leader has the responsibility to keep the team focused on the significant cause(s) highlighted by the cause-and-effect analysis. Action items that directly address causes have the best chance of culminating in successful reduction in the level of the problem.

Implementing the Plan

Up until the time implementation of corrective action actually begins, nothing that has been done under TQC/JIT has caused changes in the current system. Implementation is where attitudes and commitment are tested most severely. Even reluctant managers and employees generally will go along with TQC/JIT efforts up to this point. Except for attending meetings, analyzing data, and writing a plan, no person really has changed the way he/she does things.

Each team member should be asked to follow the plan with integrity. This means that action items must be completed on time

Activity	Person Responsible	Due Date
1. Meet all team leaders and train in purchase requisition requirements — signature cycles.	JSP/CR	Nov. 7
2. Train all department managers.	AL/KJ	Nov. 7
3. Publish memo to all employees re: requirements.	OI	Nov. 7
4. Hold weekly purchasing requisition review meetings until training review is completed.	JR	Ongoing
5. Present monitoring results.	WE	Weekly
6. Review corrective action success and continue on other causes.	Team	Weekly

Figure 3.17 Purchasing FIT Corrective Action Plan

and with sincerity. There is nothing worse for a team than to have six out of seven action items completed and to be held up for another week because one person did not take the time to do the job. Group pressures mount quickly under such circumstances.

Throughout implementation, the team continues to meet with no interruptions in schedule. The monitoring effort should continue, data plotted and reviewed each meeting along with plan implementation status.

Top-level team members should occasionally visit teams in the corrective action phase to provide encouragement and insight. Care should be taken by the TLT member not to interfere with team functioning.

Figure 3.17 is a snapshot of the purchasing FIT corrective action plan. The plan shows that the team will thoroughly inform and train as many people as possible using the new purchase requisition completion requirements. Initial focus will be on managers and other team leaders. Follow-up will be provided by one team member holding weekly purchase requisition review meetings. This activity is shown as "ongoing" indicating that until the monitoring results showed improvement, contact with those most responsible for the accuracy of purchase requisitions, managers, would be maintained. The team also is aware of the fact that they must continue to review other causes for defective purchase requisitions and that new corrective action efforts must be considered and implemented.

The team ran into some implementation barriers. It seemed that people did not want to take the time to attend training sessions. They felt the problem was a purchasing problem, not one of theirs. Purchasing FIT members attended the top-level team meeting and clarified the need for all persons invited to attend training. The TLT unanimously agreed and distributed a memorandum to all departments. The authority and commitment demonstrated by the TLT caused a flood of phone calls from people wondering when the next training session would be held. The TLT also helped by assuring that training could take place in the best conference room in the company, with coffee provided.

Similar resistance to the purchase requisition review was encountered. All members of the purchasing FIT attended every other FIT meeting in the company and explained the reason for this review. The purchasing FIT also explained that no purchase requisition would be accepted by purchasing unless submitted and reviewed during this meeting. The need for purchase requisition review meetings disappeared within several weeks.

In similar cases, teams that have recently written requirements have been known to write less powerful corrective action plans. As a word of caution, any team that believes things will improve as a result of sending newly developed requirements in the company mail to department heads will find that neither correction nor prevention will occur. The distribution of requirements should always be accompanied with a thorough training effort.

Review of Monitoring Chart for Impact

The effect of these actions was seen within two weeks. The 100 percent rejection level for purchase requisitions almost reversed to 70 percent acceptance. For a period of five consecutive weeks, not one single purchase requisition was received by purchasing without a signature. These changes were rapidly evident from the trend chart maintained weekly. The cost to review and rework purchasing requisitions dropped to less than $78 per week. Using the data in Figure 3.7, the cost of rework had dropped from an average of $492 per week ($25,584 per year) to an average of $4,056 per year. This represents over $21,500 savings per year. This savings was reflected on the cost trend line maintained by the group.

As discussed earlier, the problem of incorrect purchase requisitions seemed to be a simple one to solve.

Continuous Improvement and Prevention

Although not shown on Figure 3.17, the purchasing FIT discussed herein added several other significant preventive action items. The first was to add a page in the employee handbook which briefly clarified purchase requisition requirements to all employees. The second was the printing of this abbreviated set of requirements on the back of all purchase requisition forms. The third preventive action was to provide a trainer to all new employee orientation sessions. This trainer taught all new employees how to complete purchase requisitions in accordance with requirements.

Despite excellent early gains in quality and cost improvements, the team realized its job was not finished. The TQC/JIT environment challenges teams and individuals to continue to improve conditions until problems are put to bed. The team should not go on to new problems until the fix put in place has permanently prevented the problem from recurring. Permanent prevention may require many cycles of corrective action.

The purchasing problem presents a good example of team creativity and drive to implement continuous preventive improvement.

Analysis of Reasons for Lack of Improvement

Not all cases are so successful. Many teams find they have chosen the wrong cause, or attempted an unrealistic corrective action sequence.

In other cases, the data collected from monitoring during improvement cycles usually lags behind the activities designed to reduce time, defects, and costs. Although a team may begin corrective action, data may not reveal a shift in trend direction for several weeks. This data lag effect often is due to the fact that measurement is taking place on issues that the change has not yet impacted. Some time must be reserved, usually depending on the nature of the problem and corrective action, before judgments can be made regarding results.

Sometimes, the effect of drawing attention to a problem causes a temporary improvement effect. People have a tendency to become aware of the attention heaped on a problem area and temporarily adjust their behaviors in ways that inadvertently show up as improvements. This is known as the Hawthorne effect. Apparent improvements in such cases are not necessarily the result of corrective action. The Hawthorne effect is a good reason for teams to continue monitoring the problem's status, even after corrective action attempts have ceased. After several months, if trends show inclination to worsen, the corrective action must be reviewed to determine long-term impact.

There are other reasons for failed corrective action attempts. Occasionally, if a team is not correctly managed and the status of all corrective action activities carefully reviewed, some actions fail to get implemented or are halfheartedly implemented. The team must ensure that each step in the corrective action cycle was implemented as planned, with full competence.

The Effect of Barriers: A Study[18]

Even competent planning and implementation can fail if higher-level teams and individual managers do not help identify and remove barriers to achievement. In *Quality, Productivity and Competitive Position*, W. Edwards Deming cites the need for managers to "Remove barriers that hinder the hourly worker." Such barriers, says Deming, "rob the hourly worker of his birthright, the right to be proud of his work, the right to do a good job."[25]

From a TQC/JIT perspective, many potential corrective actions that management should take based on process control information will require changes to management's system of operation. Barriers to worker performance will exhibit themselves in many ways. Such barriers must be analyzed and conscientiously removed by higher-level teams and managers in much the same way they would demand corrective action of line personnel for other threats to quality.

In light of Deming's ideas, a study was conducted in an attempt to actually quantify barrier characteristics. The focus of the study was on manufacturing worker perspectives as might be reflected through analysis of data collected via a questionnaire. Worker attitudes can make or break a company as easily as poor financial management.

Many of the results of this study are pertinent to our discussion of why corrective action attempts do not always succeed.

Figure 3.18 is a copy of the questionnaire used. It includes 12 open-ended and forced-response structured questions covering quality in general, potential causes of defects, worker feelings about management, help available to the worker, training, and production standards.

This one-page instrument was distributed to 160 operators through their work center leads. Each questionnaire was accompanied by an envelope addressed to a mailbox so that no one else could review the respondent's answers. The manufacturer assembles large and complex electronic equipment for military application. There was some minor concern expressed that the questionnaire would raise operator expectations unrealistically, but promises were made to keep all results confidential within a restricted management group. Management was, in return, restricted from reviewing individual questionnaires which might reveal the identities of individual respondents. Overall, the questionnaire, its distribution, completion, and reporting were felt by all to be a highly sensitive issue. Sensitivity of this type was considered to be an indication of the degree of company openness with regard to quality.

A total of 127 questionnaires were returned. This accounted for 79 percent of those distributed and was considered a reasonably high response rate.

The first three questions dealt with the idea that operators occasionally need help from technically different types of people. An attempt was made to determine who operators ask for help, how often, and how they would rate the help they received.

Figures 3.19, 3.20, and 3.21 reflect operator responses to items one through three. In general, most operators said they asked their leads or foremen for help one to two times per week (1 – 2/w) or more often (up to several times per day). This is shown on Figure 3.19 for question number 1. On the average, they rated the quality of the help they received somewhat below what might be expected (Figure 3.20, question 2). Foremen rated a 7.7 out of a possible 10, while leads rated 7.4. Industrial engineers and production control personnel were rated somewhat lower.

Item 4 (Figure 3.22) showed that most operators (83.5 percent) felt they deserved credit, but somehow missed receiving that credit. Those who wrote "how" they received credit indicated that most credit was received verbally on the floor or during annual review, but letters of recommendation and promotions also were noted. One or two operators indicated that they knew they did "good" work because they saw time standards lowered.

When asked to rank items on a list which they felt caused the most defects, operators felt that parts, instructions, and poor tools contributed most. Workmanship was ranked number four and attitudes number five (Figure 3.23).

Examining these same responses in the opposite manner, operators placed less blame on wrong tools, machines (there were few machines on the floor), supervision, design, or training as cause(s) of defective work.

Since the company had no comprehensive formal training program established for assemblers, most operators indicated they

008RA.1

Product Quality Questionnaire   Work Center Number _____
                                                  Are you an Operator _____
                                                  Supervisor _____
                                                  Inspector _____
                                                  (check one)

DIRECTIONS: This survey is being taken so that you may help identify possible manufacturing quality problems.

Please answer every question to the best of your ability and as carefully and as honestly as possible. You do not have to put your name on the questionnaire, but your work center number and position will help us to determine which work areas have which type of problems. Please complete every question by placing an "X" in the correct space or by writing your best answer on the line provided.

Please complete this survey and return it in the envelope immediately!!!

QUALITY PROBLEMS: These are problems which cause you to do a poorer quality job than you really want to do. For instance, if you run a machine and it never works right, this is a quality problem.

1. How often do you request help with quality problems?

   Several times each day   _____   Once or twice each week   _____
   Once or twice a day   _____   Once or twice each month   _____
   _____   _____   Never   _____
   Other (How often?)

2. If you have problems, which one person do you usually ask for help?

   Lead   _____   Industrial Engineer (IE)   _____
   Foreman   _____   Production Control   _____
   Quality Control Engineer _____   _____   _____
   (QCE)   (Someone else . . . who?)

3. On a scale from 1 to 10 ("1" is low, "10" is high), how good is the help you receive from your:

   Lead   _____   Industrial Engineer (IE)   _____
   Foreman   _____   Production Control   _____
   Quality Control Engineer _____   _____   _____
                                              (Someone else . . . who?)

4. Do you feel that you get enough credit for doing good work?

   Never   _____   Always   _____
   Sometimes   _____
   If you checked "sometimes" or "always," how do you get credit?

   _____

   _____

Figure 3.18

(Figure 3.18 continued)

5. Mark the three (3) areas below which <u>you feel cause the most defects.</u> Put a "1" by the most frequent cause, a "2" by the next most frequent, and a "3" by the third most frequent cause.

Workmanship	_____	Design	_____
Parts	_____	Machines	_____
Kitting	_____	Training	_____
The W/C before me	_____	Supervision	_____
Poor tools	_____	Attitudes	_____
Wrong tools	_____	_____	_____
Instructions	_____	Other?	

6. Please mark the kind of training you have received at _____ . You may mark more than one.

On-the-Job (OJT)	_____	Classes attended here	_____
None	_____	Classes somewhere else	
Other	_____	but paid for by	_____
_____	_____		
(What kind?)			

7. Have you ever been told to go ahead with a defective or poor job because of production schedules?

Yes _____   No _____

8. Have you identified quality problems to someone before, and not had any help solving these problems?

Yes _____   No _____

If you marked "Yes" above, please list these problems and tell how long they have been occurring.

TYPE OF PROBLEM   SINCE (date)

_____   _____

_____   _____

_____   _____

_____   _____

9. Do you feel that production standards interfere with your ability to do your best possible work?

Yes _____   No _____

10. Do you feel that you understand what "good" quality is?

Yes _____   No _____

Explain: _____

_____

11. Please write what you feel is management's attitude toward quality. (Do you feel that management cares?)

_____

_____

_____

12. If there are other things that have not been mentioned already that you feel prevent you from putting out top quality work, please list them:

A. _____

B. _____

C. _____

D. _____

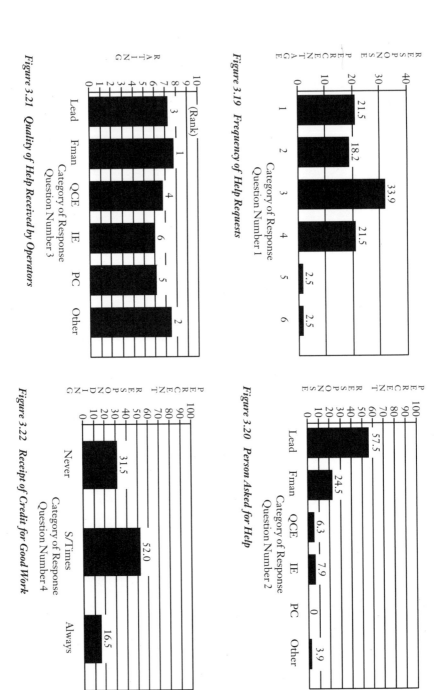

Figure 3.19 Frequency of Help Requests

Figure 3.20 Person Asked for Help

Figure 3.21 Quality of Help Received by Operators

Figure 3.22 Receipt of Credit for Good Work

received on-the-job training, while about 25 percent indicated they had some in-plant instruction.

For questions seven and eight, it was found that the majority of assemblers had not been told to proceed with a poor job due to production schedules, and that they do receive help solving quality problems when such problems are identified. On the other hand, an almost equal but slightly smaller proportion of operators revealed that they had been told to proceed with poor work and had not received help (Figures 3.24 and 3.25). In their description of problems, 52 operators listed almost every conceivable type of problem and noted that many of these problems had been around for years (or longer). Two comments indicated that these problems bother operators daily.

When asked if they feel that production standards interfere with their work, 63 percent responded "yes." Ninety-five percent of the operators checked that they knew what good quality was. Their explanations included comments such as "no defects," "good workmanship and compliance with instructions and specifications," "doing a job that I would risk my own life on," and statements such as "some or none reject from inspector and not failed during test," and "working perfect and excellent."

Question 11 received heavy input. These comments were too numerous to list. They boiled down to the general feeling that workers feel that management does want good quality, but that production schedules and delivery take priority. The large number of often-hostile responses to this item indicated that this question touched some sensitive nerves; that is, workers seemed to feel frustrated by this inconsistent dilemma.

In a catchall attempt to capture other ideas about potential or realistic barrier, item 12 asked operators for "other things . . . that you feel prevent you from putting out top quality work." Responses highlighted other potential problem areas such as:

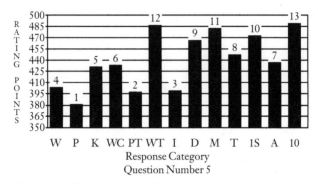

Response Category
Question Number 5

Figure 3.23   *Perceived Ranks of Causes*

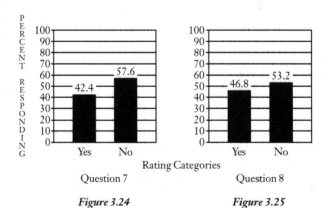

Rating Categories

Question 7   Question 8

Figure 3.24   *Figure 3.25*

Poor Job Go-Ahead and Received No Help

1. Soft attitude of management toward low-quality workers.

2. Jumping from one job to another.

3. A lack of individual incentives.

4. The need for better inspection for incoming materials.

5. Management should have better attitudes toward employee needs.

6. Buck passing, and blaming someone for poor job rather than corrective action.

7. Giving workers inconsistent verbal instructions.

8. Inconsistencies between what workers feel to be right and what is written in manufacturing instructions.

Some intercorrelations between items scaled to permit such analyses were run, and based on the statistical results, the following conclusions resulted:

1. Those operators who say they do not feel that time standards interfere with their ability to do their best possible work also are less likely to ask for help on the job than those who feel that time standards do interfere.

2. The less operators feel that they get enough credit for doing good work, the more likely they are to (a) report that they are told to go ahead with defective work, (b) feel they have identified quality problems but not received help solving them, (c) feel that production standards interfere with their abilities to do their best work, and the less likely they are to indicate that they know what good quality is.

3. There is a tendency for those operators reporting that they have been told to go ahead with poor work because of production standards to report that they have identified quality problems, but have not received help solving such problems.

From the operator's perspective, some direction emerged from the analysis.

It is important for all levels of management to provide frequent positive reinforcement (verbal or otherwise) to those who deserve it. A lack of credit for work seems to lead to attitudes that can serve as barriers.

Foremen and leads must let operators know they are willing and able to help. They must make themselves available to operators, encourage operators to request help, and at least verbally reward operators when deserved. Since most training is delivered on-the-job, workers expect and feel that they need access to and help from these important resources. A lack of access apparently serves as a barrier to worker performance.

Foremen and leads also can work to help operators by placing priority on fighting to remove or prevent defective parts from entering the line, improve manufacturing instructions, and work to improve tool quality. All of these factors are barriers to worker performance and can be improved through performance teams.

If managers feel that worker attitudes can help to improve or degrade quality, then managers must understand that worker perceptions of manager attitudes toward quality (in second place behind productivity) will be openly recognized by workers and will undoubtedly influence worker concerns for quality. Allowing work to be shipped that operators know is substandard is a sure way to convince them that managers are not concerned about quality.

Those workers who most frequently request help also are the most likely to be pressured by time standards. Leads can spend more time with them, but should not forget to give credit to the better workers. Do not take the best workers for granted.

No one should tell workers to ignore or go ahead with work which the operator perceives as poor, or they will believe that management does not care.

Deming's previously published discussions concerning worker barriers appears to have some basis in terms of worker perceptions.

The operators studied do perceive problem areas, and they do offer suggestions for improvement. They seem to feel that management places priority on shipments at the expense of quality. When they feel they don't get credit for the work they do, this feeling may be tied to their frustrations with old and recurring problems, production standards, and even their understanding of quality.

For a manager who believes that worker attitudes can be cultivated enough to help reveal and remove barriers to quality, and therefore, to the company's profitability, Deming's texts are certainly worth reading.

The manager who chooses to ignore human needs for a "pat on the back" and is willing to knowingly ship substandard product when everyone in the plant knows this happens, should not expect employees to do anything but follow this leadership style.

There is a more critical message that should be presented here. If management doesn't appear to care, what will make the workers care? The answer is, nothing. Managers reading this should seriously consider this dilemma. The people who work for you already know this. Managers train their people to perform according to their own values. If managers want to knowingly ship defective product, they have absolutely no right or recourse when defective product is built by the people who report to them. This is completely a management-controlled problem, caused by management, and potentially solved by management. The buck stops there.

During the cause-and-effect analysis exercise, if the team has failed to identify a significant cause for the overall problem, corrective action will be focused on an apparent or intuitively logical cause that does not account for a significant proportion of the defects, costs, or lost time. The result will be little or no discernible change in the monitoring trend line. In such cases, the team may become frustrated in their attempts to correct the problem.

There are more sophisticated statistical techniques that help to determine significant contributors to effects. For example, control charts may be set up to help identify smaller parts of the process which may be yielding excessive rejects, dollar losses, or time delays. Additionally, t-tests, analysis of variance techniques, regression analysis, and multivariate statistical techniques can be utilized to help determine significant contributors to process variability. Such topics are beyond the scope of this text, but experts are available to help establish the proper experimentation, data collection, and analysis techniques.

Some words of caution are valuable at this point. Most of the more advanced statistical techniques mentioned are intended to help determine the extent of the relationship between variables. The conclusion may not be made that if a significant statistical relationship between variables is found, one variable causes the other to react in certain ways. The nature of the mathematics underlying most statistical techniques allows no such conclusions to be drawn. Statistical techniques allow inferences to be drawn only when used in conjunction with tightly controlled experiments. Even "tightly controlled experiments" have weaknesses and may result in incorrect interpretations.

Again, with a competent analyst in tow, reasonably good conclusions can be reached. Not only will a competent statistician help design the experiment with good controls, but appropriate statistical tools will be applied, and, even more importantly, the probability of spurious interpretations will be minimized. Simply stated, this means that if someone has an idea they think will work, they tend to lose objectivity when conducting experiments. Often, it can be said, they found the results for which they were looking. Unfortunately, in such cases the truth fails to be discovered. Most novice researchers reveal their inexperience with the simple statement, "This proves it!" Statistics and research never "prove" anything, they are merely tools to help better understand the situation.

Perhaps the most common reason for a lack of results from corrective action arises from a lack of focus on the team's part. Many teams, in their exuberance to solve the problem, simply tackle too many potential causes at one time. Usually, this results in no measurable impact. It is comparable to the team taking a handful of seeds and throwing them over a square mile of ground. The team's energies and efforts are thinned out to the point that nothing changes. Such teams will burn out after two to three months and will consider the entire effort a waste of time. Maintaining focus on one problem, one significant cause, and one concentrated corrective action attempt is critical.

CORRECTIVE ACTION TEAM (CAT) IMPLEMENTATION

The previous discussion followed the flowchart shown as Figure 3.1. This complete series of activities was described as it applies to functional improvement teams (FIT). Figure 3.26 is an almost identical flowchart which depicts the flow of activities required for CAT activities.

Chapter 2 describes organizational activities relative to all team structures and functioning. There it was noted that CATs were formed by the top-level team (TLT). Further, these teams were formed based on problem identification by the TLT. Basically, this means that the top part of Figure 3.26 is complete prior to team implementation. The activities that the TLT follow to identify team members, team leader, and even secretary are simply to appoint these persons.

With one or two minor exceptions the remainder of the flowchart activities are identical to those described for FIT implementation. Identical tools, forms, and thought processes should occur throughout the cycle of continuous improvement.

All CAT reporting should be directly to the TLT. CAT leaders are responsible to TLT decisions and should be invited to report CAT status TLT meetings on a regular basis. The TLT is responsible, in turn, for making sure that barriers to CAT progress are removed or resolved.

The only other notable difference between FIT and CAT implementation appears as the last step in Figure 3.26. When the TLT decides that the problem is solved, the CAT is disbanded and the TLT may organize another CAT to address a new problem.

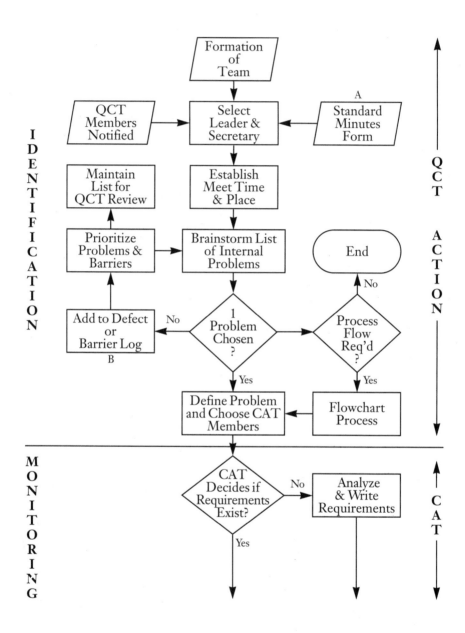

Figure 3.26

(Figure 3.26 continued)

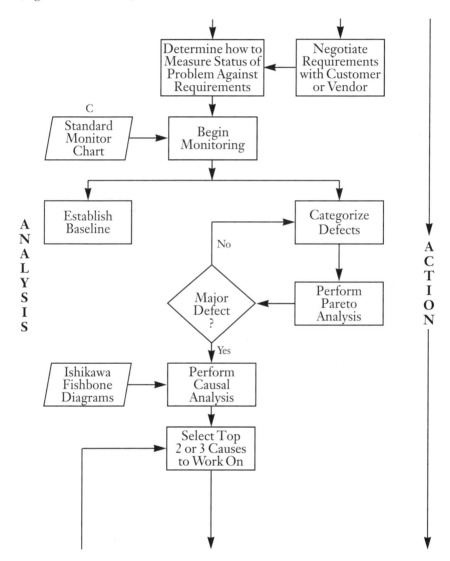

(Figure 3.26 continued)

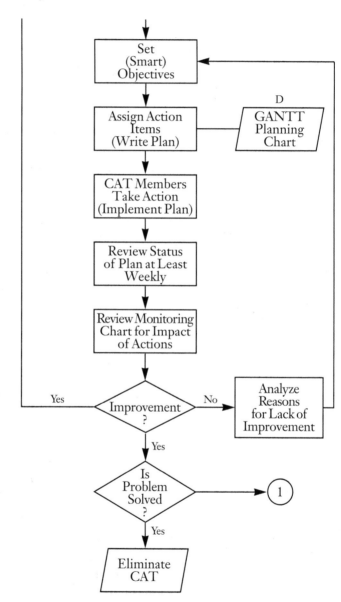

SUMMARY

Resolution of many business problems do not require employing TQC/JIT system principles and practices. The establishment of an organizational structure that encourages teamwork, the planning for continuous improvement, and the various implementation details employed are not required for many business decisions. Where management successfully leads employees in a positive, "We can!" atmosphere of achievement, where quality is demanded every day in every way, where conscientious training is in place, where barriers are identified and removed by management, where departments and management groups work together to solve problems, customers will look for and find superior products and services. Such companies are rare.

The steps outlined as a systematic way to achieve quality and time improvements resulting in profitable business enterprises, are critical to those less fortunate organizations which need desperately to develop a systematic culture capable of competing.

Chapter 3 offered a reasonably simple sequential approach to TQC/JIT implementation. None of the steps presented are mandatory, but all have been proven time and again to help. All the steps are tools of TQC/JIT. Continuous improvement is a never-ending job. TQC/JIT are never-ending systems of activities, not projects to be completed.

The general implementation phase including organizing, planning, prioritizing, measuring, analyzing symptoms and causes, and preventing future losses follow a logical sequence. This sequence of activities needs to be realistically viewed as failure prone. When desired effects are not realized, people need to be challenged to try again, not berated for failing. Failure is learning. Team failure can most often be attributed to management's failure to help remove barriers to achievement.

4

Specialized Teams

*T*his chapter provides specific TQC/JIT team suggestions reflecting the concepts and philosophy outlined in Chapter 1, the organizational structure outlined in Chapter 2, and the tools used in CAT and FIT implementation activities outlined in Chapter 3. The special teams discussed in this chapter are focused on methods for solving manufacturing problems most commonly associated with TQC/JIT concepts. These are primarily preventive teams whose functions are to cost-effectively use TQC/JIT tools to help the company achieve and continue to maintain profitability.

JIT manufacturing lines often are considered to be an interim step between labor-intensive mass production or assembly and fully automated assembly. The list of teams noted in Table 4.1 could be expanded or reduced depending on the particular company situation. For example, Chapter 12 of the *Tool and Manufacturing Engineers Handbook, Volume 4 (Quality Control and Assembly)*, shows excellent specific examples of many of the concepts presented in this chapter.[22]

Table 4.1   Specialized Teams

Team Focus	Recommended Members
Pilot line	PROD/ENG/QUAL/PC
Vendor relationships	PROD/ENG/QUAL/PUR/PC
Value engineering	PROD/ENG/QUAL/PUR/DES
Design for manufacturability	PROD/ENG/QUAL/DES
Parts commonality	ENG/DES
Preventive maintenance	PROD/MAINT
Foolproofing (Poka-Yoke)	PROD/QUAL/ENG/DES
Process layout and line balance	PROD/ENG
Lot size reduction	PROD/PC
Organize and clean workplace	PROD/ENG
KANBAN	PROD/PC/PUR
Line stop	PROD/QUAL
Statistical process control	PROD/QUAL
Visual signals (ANDON)	PROD/QUAL
Training (certification)	PROD
Setup time reduction	PROD/ENG
Automation review	PROD/ENG
Cycle time control	PROD/ENG
Manufacturing focused	

Our current interest is in the teams shown in Figure 1.1, page 6. The team foci shown in the left-hand column are a list of the major problem areas that need to be addressed during TQC/JIT implementation with an increasing emphasis on JIT manufacturing requirements. In each case, it is recommended that the team be formed, either as a corrective action team (CAT) or a functional improvement team (FIT). Such specialized teams have the job of studying each issue and developing and implementing a plan along with appropriate measurement and analysis methods. These team activities can be short or long term. For example, in most companies, a vendor team will have to completely redesign the way a company perceives or deals with vendors, thus taking two or three years. A lot-size reduction team, however, may make rapid progress and reach the ideal one assembly at a time lot size in a few weeks.

The right-hand column in Table 4.1 lists which departments should provide members to each team. These members are only recommended. Each company should decide on the appropriate members for each team.

The main emphasis of this chapter is to briefly describe each team's activities relative to the focus noted in Table 4.1. In general, the team members are expected to follow the basic implementation strategies outlined in Chapter 3. Often, however, these teams can and do use a variety of engineering, design, quality, or production tools and techniques which are beyond the scope of this book.

Despite the fact that the team problem already should have been defined by the TLT or some other team, the team generally starts with trying to determine some method of problem measurement. For instance, the lot-size reduction team has an objective of reducing lot sizes. Reduced lot sizes result in lower cycle times, less inventory, and a number of other easily measured management parameters. After the lot sizes are measured, either defect or cycle analyses may be performed, cause-and-effects analyzed, corrective action planned and implemented. The continuous cycle of improvement is followed until the desired improvements are achieved.

The top-level team should be aware of some additional concerns when preparing to implement TQC/JIT in a manufacturing environment. Table 4.2 summarizes some of the key points.

Table 4.2   Top-Level Team Implementation Concerns

1. Special resources must be identified and dedicated to the implementation effort.

2. Worker ownership of the line and participation in all aspects of function and improvement with authority over the line is mandatory.

3. There must be an ongoing, continuous worker effort to refine the process.

4. Output of the line is deemphasized; linear flow is emphasized.

5. Rigid job classifications must be eliminated through cross training.

6. There must be a development of mutual trust between the implementing organization and its vendors and customers.

All of the items in Table 4.2 have been discussed elsewhere in this book with the exception of points four and six. The idea that linearity of production rather than sheer volume must be emphasized causes most production managers to choke, but the redirection in emphasis is critical. Linearity results in increased productivity. That's the purpose of the whole system: fast-flowing, error-free products and services.

Trust between an organization and its customers and vendors always has been important. Trust, however, goes beyond buying customers lunch and dinner. In this case, trust means such things as sharing the delivery schedule with your vendors so they have a better idea when the ramp and slowdowns will come. It also means not returning good materials under false quality pretenses because you reach an inventory overage situation.

THE PILOT LINE

One concept that is important to consider for any organization attempting to implement TQC/JIT concepts on a manufacturing floor using the following ideas and teams described, is the concept of a pilot line. A mini-version or experimental manufacturing line can be set up and manipulated prior to major changes to main manufacturing floor layouts. The manufacturing changes approved by experimenters and managers for the pilot line often are implemented across the floor.

Even with a pilot line, however, individual functional improvement or corrective action teams should be experimenting and changing their own lines for improvement purposes. Successful FIT ideas should be tested on the pilot line accompanied by objective data collection in order to determine the ability of each change to be successfully reproduced.

The pilot line is a critical and useful concept. The effects of product mix changes on a JIT line may be evaluated. Lot sizes may be played with; foolproofed parts and tooling, line balances and layouts changed; statistical process control conditions established; and any of a number of other team effects may be evaluated. The pilot line should serve as the place to experiment in a controlled condition environment.

VENDOR RELATIONSHIPS

All manufacturing or assembly companies require good vendor relationships. Most companies consider good vendor relationships a valuable and necessary part of business, but also consider vendors to be a lower-class animal capable of being disposed of or otherwise mistreated as whim dictates. If the market is rising, vendors are to be ramped up quickly, prices driven down, one played off against the other. Such companies like to have a number of vendors for any particular part number. More vendors are required to fulfill the schedule juggling, price pressures, quality fallouts, and delivery misses. Frivolous afterthoughts such as quality are tolerated within the confines of "making the schedule." The buyer's reputation and success in such companies is measured primarily in terms of percent price reductions acquired throughout the fiscal year. Even companies which claim "Quality, Delivery, Price" as being the order of priority for vendor qualification and certification, generally end up with price or delivery as the operational priority. No company serious about a TQC/JIT program can deal with vendors in such ways.

Some basic ideas with regard to a TQC/JIT vendor relationship include limiting the number of vendors, preferably to one for each type of part. Limiting vendors means engineers, quality engineers, buyers, etc., can spend more time with each vendor working preventive issues.

Companies with large vendor bases rarely are able to provide the support required by each vendor, even in relatively simple terms such as calibration and inspection correlation, as well as in more complex terms like cleaning up designs prior to vendor production. Consider a single vendor quality engineer with 15 vendors and 15 part numbers with which to deal. In the simplest form this means one must deal with 225 (15 × 15) different problems. Each vendor has a different process capable of holding different tolerances on the parts in question. Probably every vendor will want to argue tolerance changes to different dimensions. This means that a single engineer can have thousands of decisions to make with no real way to track or verify the validity of the decisions. This is an impossible position for an engineer to be placed in, but most companies operate this way.

The vendor's location relative to the customer's manufacturing operation often is considered significant. The closer the two operations are to each other, the quicker lots can be moved from the vendor to the customer. This means, in turn, that lots can be smaller in size and more frequent in shipment. This strategy is consistent with JIT concepts and helps to keep interfacility inventory levels low and flowing to the JIT beat. As mentioned in Chapter 1, the concept of control over inventory levels, rapid inventory turns, and material flow applies to the entire stream of product manufacturing, not just to work-in-process.

The process for qualifying and certifying vendors is an important issue in a TQC/JIT environment. There is nothing like sitting in a meeting where a purchasing representative and the sales representative from a prospective vendor are actively engaged in discussions. Needless to say, the absence of other departmental representatives indicates that such discussions will not adequately cover important topics. In many companies, purchasing is handled by the purchasing department and other departments rarely are involved. This lack of interdepartmental participation on the part of both companies seems intuitively to be a limited approach because purchasing generally has price-dominated objectives and the vendor has profit objectives. The necessary checks and balances are missing.

To some vendors, the "checks" represent nothing but "trendy BS" or paper mills. Usually this is because the vendor either doesn't understand the checks or because the vendor is too small to implement the sophisticated control systems required to do business with large companies. This can be a frustrating situation for a vendor; trying to grow, but not being able to keep up with new demands.

For some customers, team-oriented management is not part of the management style currently dominating the organization. Each department has its own job, generally not to be interfered with or trespassed upon by another department.

The purchasing-sales interface seems, logically, to be such a limited approach that potential disasters may remain hidden until it is too late. Purchased parts, their prices, delivery, and quality affect all parts of a customer's activities. Trying to prevent problems that are caused by purchased parts is a monumental task which requires that many of the company's resources are organized and directed in a cohesive, teamlike manner.

For those individuals lucky enough to work for companies with their acts together, the meetings between vendors and customers are team oriented from both sides. Issues are brought up and discussed, sometimes with new ideas and procedures being exchanged. Such exchanges from multiple perspectives are beneficial.

In addition to some of the steps just outlined, there are several basic steps that should be considered in order to bring a vendor up to quality and delivery levels that will reduce total costs.

A standardized vendor qualification and certification procedure should be written and followed (See Appendix E for an example). Vendors should be certified by a team of representatives from the customer company. This team should use a standardized vendor qualification survey form (Appendix F) and data should be analyzed to rank vendors for their support capabilities. This form should be designed so that scores will reflect the vendor's ability to prevent problems (as outlined in Chapter 1) and can be expanded to include analyses of vendor JIT capabilities.

A company's receiving inspection group should have a twofold goal. First, receiving inspection should protect the production line from ever being negatively impacted by bad parts. That is, the production line is to be treated as the receiving inspection's customer. The words "negatively impacted" imply that the production line should be able to achieve the most cost-effective manufacturing position possible. Receiving inspection should, in part, be evaluated based on its ability to consistently supply the line with parts that are determined, through cost analyses (Chapter 5) procedures, to be the most optimal solution to reducing costs.

A fraction defective (P) chart (see *Process Quality Control* by Ellis Ott for examples of control charts) should be supplied that plots one point for each lot (by part number) shipped by each vendor.[11] If a vendor does not supply P charts with each shipment, the company must implement a procedure which plots such data in their own receiving inspection area. A standardized sample size should be established which adequately reflects the status of multiple lots. This sample probably should range between 100 and 200 pieces. Standardizing sample sizes helps to stabilize control limit calculations which are a function of sample size. Control limits should be calculated and drawn on each chart and the percent defective should be clearly shown for each lot. In addition to the plotted point, the vendor should show the actual percent of defects value.

Mean and range charts should be developed for critical piece part parameters. Vendors can be asked to take small samples, hopefully in their process after each operation, and plot these data on control charts. Control limits, average lines, and tolerance limits should be placed on the chart. These charts should be submitted to customers with every shipment along with P charts that resulted from the vendor's final inspection.

Vendors capable and willing to submit control charts showing their processes' abilities to control critical parameters are rare. When a company locates a vendor who will fulfill this requirement, the vendor is probably trustworthy. Such a vendor probably will believe your offer to work together to solve problems, and, in spite of occasional out-of-control conditions, will provide the customer with quality product on a consistent basis.

Additionally, all vendors should be helped to achieve a dock-to-stock status. This implies that the receiving inspection group is constantly working to reduce its own workload so that time is available to develop new procedures. Preventive time must be available for planning to bring new vendors on board through standardized qualification and certification procedures.

Vendors should understand and be committed to helping a customer achieve just-in-time material deliveries as part of the dock-to-stock program. Thinking about JIT material deliveries and dock-to-stock are pipe dreams for most American companies. These words are seen in the literature, but most managers feel that such concepts have little relevance to their own operations; they are concepts the Japanese developed, and because of their culture, will work only for them. This is an unfortunate feeling as this belief forever dooms managers from achieving such heights. From the standpoint of customer-vendor relations dock-to-stock and JIT are long-term strategies directed at continuous improvement.

VALUE ENGINEERING

Value engineering refers to the concept that parts can be redesigned in any of several ways to reduce the overall cost of either the parts or manufacturing processes using the parts. Included in value engineering are design for manufacturability (again the emphasis is on cost reduction) and parts commonality. A functional analysis of the parts usually results in a redesign effort which is supposed to result in fewer, cheaper parts required to build the end product.[23] Decisions are reached based on value improvement (cost reduction). In addition to lower part costs, value may be improved through quality and time requirement reduction improvements. Regardless of the emotional beauty of a design change, if costs do not decrease, changes are not made.

Redesign can be accomplished using computers to model the parts as well as the manufacturing processes. Computer models keep costs low by helping design parts and processes which are capable of avoiding manufacturing errors.

Consideration is given to how parts are held; their symmetry (if reversible, they can be assembled in either direction; if irreversible, they cannot be assembled backward; a form of foolproofing); their orientation in transit, in fixtures, and in assembly; insertion methods; joining methods and other strategies are employed.

Value engineering is a major effort. It is long term in nature and is considered an integral part of TQC/JIT.

DESIGN FOR MANUFACTURABILITY

The team assigned to work design for manufacturability issues usually includes members from the production, engineering, quality, and design groups. The group is assembled and challenged with examining product designs which can be modified in order to simplify manufacturing.

One Korean disk drive manufacturer has successfully reduced the number of to-be-assembled components from over 50 to 27.

This same manufacturer, because of its superior design for manufacturing, has been able to build and implement a manufacturing line which went from a capability of 1,500 drives a month in the third month to over 17,000 drives a month in the fifth month.

This ability to ramp manufacturing and put out large quantities of reliable product in a short period of time at low costs is considered absolutely necessary in the rapidly changing Winchester disk drive industry. The single design for manufacturability approach applied to this company helped it to gain market share with good profit margins. At the outset, other drive manufacturers had little confidence that this approach could work. Now many more drive companies are interested in taking the time to work out their product designs prior to spending millions of dollars on tooling and manufacturing lines dedicated to building defects.

PARTS COMMONALITY

Teams with the responsibility for developing common or generic parts for different final products can save companies large amounts of money. By focusing the efforts of engineering and design personnel, standardization of parts can occur which will meet customer and manufacturing requirements.

The team begins with a review of all similar drawings, separating them into common piles. The next stage is to determine which dimensions can be standardized on all parts represented. Suggestions should be written up and purchasing should be invited for review and for further suggestions.

Parts commonality is often an idea that is acceptable to purchasing personnel, regardless of their dedication to TQC/JIT. Parts commonality gives them greater purchasing power (thus helping them to achieve annual cost reduction objectives) and control over vendors. The fact that common parts configurations can be standardized means that they can be purchased from a reduced number of vendors (another positive approach to TQC/JIT).

PREVENTIVE MAINTENANCE

The general concept of prevention was discussed in detail in Chapter 1. Preventive maintenance refers to a specific type of prevention, that of continuously providing manufacturing with tooling, equipment, and machinery which has had periodic preventive maintenance. This function usually is under the control of the engineering group, but is more often nonexistent. When the preventive maintenance function is nonexistent, tools and equipment are allowed to be used until they are out of adjustment or alignment, thus contributing their own share to process variability.

Preventive maintenance is not a glamorous job. Engineering does not find significant reward in inspecting and reworking old tooling.

Regardless of attitudes, a TQC/JIT team needs to be formed to ensure that no fixture, tool, machine, or even soldering tip is left in a production line to be used until it begins causing defects. A simple schedule of maintenance can be agreed on by the production and maintenance teams (which may include a quality engineer and a manufacturing engineer). Some tools and equipment must be studied to determine the amount of wear that is allowable before removal from the line. Certainly, production must have spares to keep production going during maintenance, or maintenance must be performed during nonworking hours.

Every effort should be made to schedule, check, and maintain such tooling, equipment, or fixturing. Automobiles and aircraft, as examples, require periodic preventive maintenance. Certainly, many people have at some time in their lives experienced the failure of some automotive part which would not have failed if preventive maintenance had been scheduled. Most of today's automobile manufacturers will not award repair costs to individuals whose vehicles have broken down from a lack of preventive maintenance. Certainly, no one would like to fly on an airplane that had not gone through needed maintenance. The same principles hold true for manufacturing equipment.

FOOLPROOFING

The concept of foolproofing basically means to look at any process carefully enough to see how operators might be making mistakes because they must make decisions which can be eliminated. For instance, suppose that a part might be placed in a fixture upside-down. If the fixture could be modified so that it would be impossible to place the part in an upside-down manner, the fixture would have been foolproofed.

Administrative activities can also be foolproofed to some extent. Forms that are to be filled out often contain incomplete information. The incompleteness of the form often causes its rejection and rework. This causes delays in approval and high rework costs. The form could be simplified so that every block must be completed, or a printed screen can shield those parts which do not have to be completed. This would leave only the parts that must be completed with room to write.

The intensive purposeful search for areas of a company that can be foolproofed is a special team activity, but with good training, any individual can begin immediately to work up foolproofing ideas and solutions. In manufacturing, production, quality, engineering, and design personnel are often challenged to perform complete operation-by-operation reviews of tooling and fixturing with the purpose of foolproofing.

PROCESS LAYOUT AND LINE BALANCE

In Chapter 1, the concept of line balance was introduced with the intent that the process should be synchronized: "All parts of the process should be producing to the same heartbeat." A smooth flow of materials from operator to operator was envisioned.

A team formed to accomplish the task of process layout and line balance usually is comprised of members from production and engineering. Operators, as well as production personnel and an engineer or two, must be challenged to break up large floor layouts into

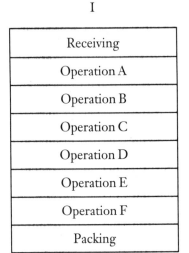

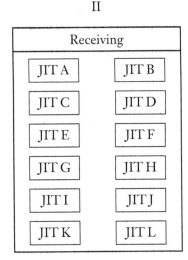

Figure 4.1   Floor Layout

smaller, multiple operation lines with product and volume flexibility. Figure 4.1 (example of a change implemented in Mexico) contrasts two floor setups. Figure 4.1 (I) shows a setup with thousands of parts each hour being pushed through a manufacturing line with cycle times in weeks and inventory levels in millions of dollars.

Figure 4.1(II) shows a floor layout which provides more output per hour, one hour cycle times, and barely enough inventory to work on per lot, thus reducing inventory levels to dollars instead of millions of dollars. The JIT modules governed by TQC principles in Figure 4.1(II) include packing within the line which prevents further transportation and handling problems. Each module is supplied materials on a pull basis, product is built, and packed on the floor. Each module contains exactly the same operations as Figure 4.1(I) setup but is flexible enough to handle all of the same part number or a group of different part number configurations.

Most teams must be told that their task is to take each manufacturing operation, and match it in hourly volume capabilities with every other operation until a minimum line size is achieved. For example, if in Table 4.3, column I, the following operations and operator ratios were found on a factory floor, the resulting initial JIT line could look like column II.

Table 4.3   Line Balance Example

I		II	
Original Floor		JIT Layout	
Operation	Number	Operation	Number
A	20	A	1
B	40	B	2
C	300	C	15
D	30	D	1.5
E	100	E	5
F	75	F	3.75

If the number of operators in the smallest sized operation on the original floor is divided into the number of operators for each other operation, column D results. As an example, on the original floor, 20 operators work in workcenter or operation A while 40 work in operation B. If 40 is divided by 20, the result is 2. Only one A operator is needed to put out enough product or to balance the two operators in operation B, who now balance the 15 in operation C, etc.

Notice that for operation D, 1.5 operators is not a satisfactory number since one-half of an operator is not available. One solution is to double all numbers in column II which results in rounded whole numbers. Another solution is to find a way to reduce the staff-hours (simplify, combine, or eliminate) required by operation D, thus bringing the line into balance.

Figure 4.2 shows one organization's analysis of a nine-operation

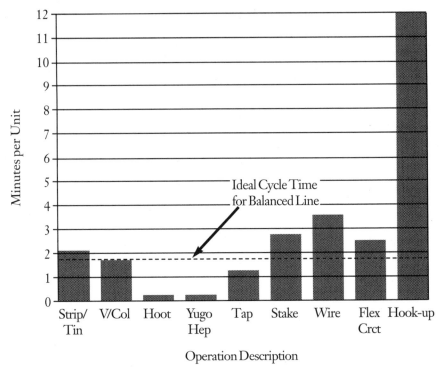

Figure 4.2   Typical Line Balance

manufacturing stream. The problem was given the minutes per unit figures for each operation, to determine an ideal cycle time for a balanced line. The ideal cycle time is shown as a dotted line drawn across the chart. In this case, the resulting work flow ended up looking like Figure 4.3. Although not completely balanced, this is a good starting place for the team to continue improvement attempts. It is obvious from Figure 4.2 that some of the first five operations will be under and over staffed. This would be a perfect time for the team to consider recombining, eliminating, and simplifying some operations to improve the balance.

Once some sort of numbers balance is achieved, the team has the task of making a paper model of the floor layout. This is best

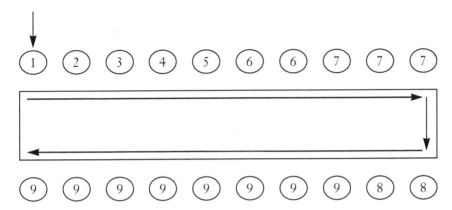

Figure 4.3 Resulting Work Flow

accomplished by having each team member independently come up with a solution that shows the number of people required by the line balance problem and also uses actual work stations, machinery, etc. This exercise should get the team to devise and agree on the smallest and simplest floor layout that will effectively utilize equipment and machinery without drastically increasing costs.

Figures 4.4 through 4.9 are Korean examples of the plans developed by six different individuals in their attempts to plan a layout. The layout is drawn with operations labeled. The dimensions of the layouts are shown, including square foot calculations. Also included are the number of operators required based on estimated quantities to be built per day (estimated output) and estimated hours per unit to build. Output targets are stated and a complete tooling and equipment list is established which shows the availability, cost, lead time for missing tooling, and the department responsible for selecting and ordering.

From a pure material flow outlook, the most promising layouts are shown in patterns E and F. Both of these require tunnel ovens which require 20 weeks to order and deliver. To begin with an earlier pattern (A through F) with the intent to move into either pattern E or F would show futuristic planning while allowing a quick conversion

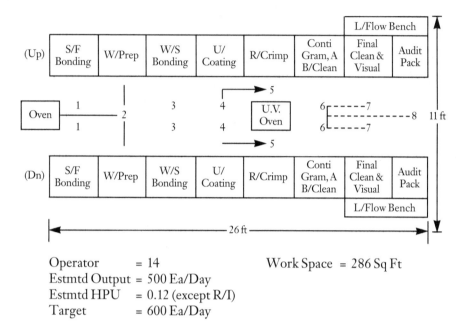

Operator   = 14   Work Space = 286 Sq Ft
Estmtd Output = 500 Ea/Day
Estmtd HPU   = 0.12 (except R/I)
Target   = 600 Ea/Day

Required Tools and Equipment

#	Tooling/Equip	Qty	Avail	Unavail	Lead Time	Cost	Responsible
1	Bonding Fixture	600		X	6 Wks	$4000	Engr
2	Wire Prep Board	10	X				
3	Wire Bonder	2	X				
4	W/B Fixture	2		X	6 Wks	500	Engr
5	U/C Fixture	2		X		500	
6	'L' Meter	2	(1)	X	8 Wks		(Order)
7	Gram Machine	2		X	8 Wks		(Order)
8	Clean Rack	20		X	6 Wks	300	Engr
9	Ultr C/Tank	2		X	8 Wks		(Order)
10	L/Flow Bench	2		X	8 Wks	1500	(Order)
11	20X Scope	13	X				
12	Oven	2	1	X	8 Wks	700	(Ordered)
13	Bag Seal'g Machine	1	(1)	1	3 Wks	250	(Ordered)

Figure 4.4   Pattern A

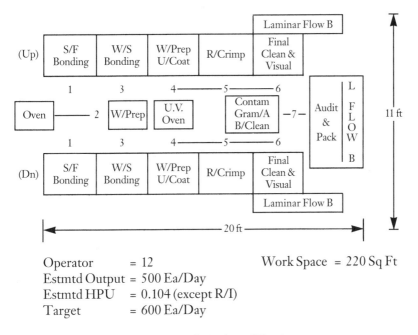

Operator   = 12   Work Space = 220 Sq Ft
Estmtd Output = 500 Ea/Day
Estmtd HPU   = 0.104 (except R/I)
Target   = 600 Ea/Day

Required Tools and Equipment

#	Tooling/Equip	Qty	Avail	Unavail	Lead Time	Cost	Responsible
1	Bonding Fixture	600		X	6 Wks	$4000	Engr
2	Wire Prep Board	10	X				
3	Wire Bonder	2	X				
4	W/B Fixture	2		X	6 Wks	500	Engr
5	U/C Fixture	2		X	6 Wks	500	Engr
6	'L' Meter	1	(1)	X	8 Wks		(Order)
7	Gram Machine	1		X	8 Wks		(Order)
8	Clean Rack	20		X	6 Wks	300	Engr
9	Ultr C/Tank	1		X	8 Wks		(Order)
10	L/Flow Bench	3		X	8 Wks	1500	(Order)
11	20X Scope	10	X				
12	Oven	2	(1)	X	8 Wks	700	(Ordered)
13	Bag Seal'g Machine	1	(1)	1	3 Wks	250	(Ordered)

Figure 4.5   Pattern B

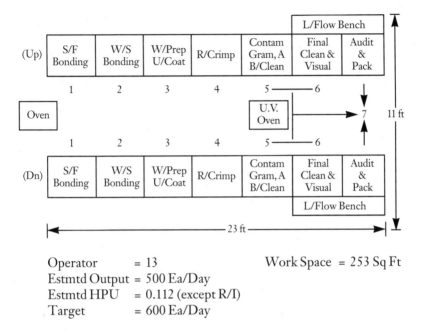

Operator   = 13   Work Space = 253 Sq Ft
Estmtd Output = 500 Ea/Day
Estmtd HPU   = 0.112 (except R/I)
Target   = 600 Ea/Day

Required Tools and Equipment

#	Tooling/Equip	Qty	Avail	Unavail	Lead Time	Cost	Responsible
1	Bonding Fixture	600		X	6 Wks	$4000	Engr
2	Wire Prep Board	10	X				
3	Wire Bonder	2	X				
4	W/B Fixture	2		X	6 Wks	500	Engr
5	U/C Fixture	2		X	6 Wks	500	
6	'L' Meter	2	(1)	X	8 Wks		(Order)
7	Gram Machine	2		X	8 Wks		(Order)
8	Clean Rack	20		X	6 Wks	300	Engr
9	Ultr C/Tank	2		X	8 Wks		(Order)
10	L/Flow Bench	2		X	8 Wks		(Order)
11	20X Scope	10	X				
12	Oven	2	(1)	X	8 Wks	700	(Ordered)
13	Bag Seal'g Machine	1	(1)	1	3 Wks	250	(Ordered)

Figure 4.6   Pattern C

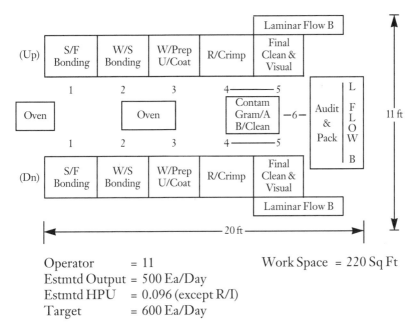

Operator   = 11   Work Space = 220 Sq Ft
Estmtd Output = 500 Ea/Day
Estmtd HPU   = 0.096 (except R/I)
Target   = 600 Ea/Day

Required Tools and Equipment

#	Tooling/Equip	Qty	Avail	Unavail	Lead Time	Cost	Responsible
1	Bonding Fixture	400		X	6 Wks	$4000	Engr
2	Wire Prep Board	10	X				
3	Wire Bonder	2	X				
4	W/B Fixture	2		X	6 Wks	500	Engr
5	U/C Fixture	2		X	6 Wks	500	Engr
6	'L' Meter	1	(1)	X	8 Wks		(Order)
7	Gram Machine	1	(1)	X	8 Wks		(Order)
8	Clean Rack	20		X	6 Wks	300	Engr
9	Ultr C/Tank	1		X	8 Wks		(Order)
10	L/Flow Bench	3		X	8 Wks		(Order)
11	20X Scope	9	X				
12	Oven	2	(1)	X	8 Wks	700	(Ordered)
13	Bag Seal'g Machine	1	(1)	1	3 Wks	250	(Ordered)

Figure 4.7 Pattern D

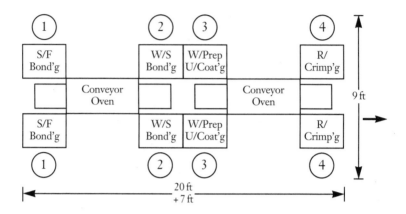

Operator   = 11   Work Space   = 243 Sq Ft
Estmtd Output = 500 Up/500 Dn
Estmtd HPU   = 0.096 (except R/I)
Target   = 600/600 Daily

Required Tools and Equipment

#	Tooling/Equip	Qty	Avail	Unavail	Lead Time	Cost	Responsible
1	Bonding Fixture	600		X	6 Wks	$4000	Engr
2	Wire Prep Board	10	X				
3	Wire Bonder	2	X				
4	W/B Fixture	2		X	6 Wks	500	Engr
5	U/C Fixture	2		X	6 Wks	500	Engr
6	'L' Meter	1	(1)	X	8 Wks		(Order)
7	Gram Machine	1		X	8 Wks		(Order)
8	Clean Rack	20		X	6 Wks	300	Engr
9	Ultr C/Tank	1		X	8 Wks		(Order)
10	L/Flow Bench	1		X	8 Wks		(Order)
11	20X Scope	9	X				
12	Tunnel Oven	2		X	20 Wks		(Order)
13	Bag Seal'g Machine	1	(1)	X	3 Wks	250	(Order)

Figure 4.8   Pattern E

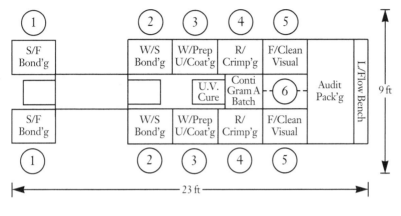

Operator   = 11   Work Space = 207 Sq Ft
Estmtd Output = 500 Up/500 Dn Daily
Estmtd HPU   = 0.096 (except R/I)
Target   = 600/600 Daily

Required Tools and Equipment

#	Tooling/Equip	Qty	Avail	Unavail	Lead Time	Cost	Responsible
1	Bonding Fixture	600		X	6 Wks	$4000	Engr
2	Wire Prep Board	10	X				
3	Wire Bonder	2	X				
4	W/B Fixture	2		X	6 Wks	500	Engr
5	U/C Fixture	2		X	6 Wks	500	Engr
6	'L' Meter	1	(1)	X	8 Wks		(Order)
7	Gram Machine	1		X	8 Wks		(Order)
8	Clean Rack	20		X	6 Wks	300	Engr
9	Ultr C/Tank	1		X	8 Wks		Engr
10	L/Flow Bench	1		X	8 Wks		(Order)
11	20X Scope	9	X				
12	Tunnel Oven	1		X	20 Wks		(Order)
13	Oven	1	X		8 Wks	700	(Order)
14	Bag Seal'g Machine	1	(1)	X	3 Wks	250	(Order)

Figure 4.9   Pattern F

to a JIT module using existing equipment. Pattern F will require the least amount of work space to build the same quantity of product per day as the other lines.

Other patterns can be criticized based on costs associated with start-up or the lack of linearity. For example, pattern D requires only 220 square feet, but shows two ovens, which could conceivably be reduced to one.

After each team member has developed his/her own version on paper, each one takes a turn at the white board showing the plan to the rest of the team. The team critiques, measures, and works over every layout presented. In this manner, even the worst appearing plan often ends up being the best because it needs team thinking to help it achieve reduction touches. After all plans are presented, the team votes to accept one.

The chosen layout should be reviewed in light of actual manufacturing floor spaces to ensure that it can be duplicated repeatedly across and down the manufacturing floor (Figure 4.10).

The flip-flop capability of small JIT-type line layouts often allows for the sharing of larger or more expensive equipment and machinery (Figure 4.10).

Facility layout is another issue which must be considered. Material flow should be smooth, whether through a line or through an entire factory. Figure 4.11 shows a two-story building with a poor material flow (although similar examples exist in many places, this particular example was observed in a Hong Kong electronics manufacturing facility). Material goes upstairs, downstairs, back upstairs, back downstairs, etc. This is ridiculous and shows that no one has looked at or planned for material flow for some time. Simple is better. Figure 4.12 cleans up the 4.11 mess.

Line balance and floor layout problems require a team effort! Such problems can generate the greatest motivation and creativity in all TQC/JIT activities. Solutions also provide the greatest manpower, material, and space savings.

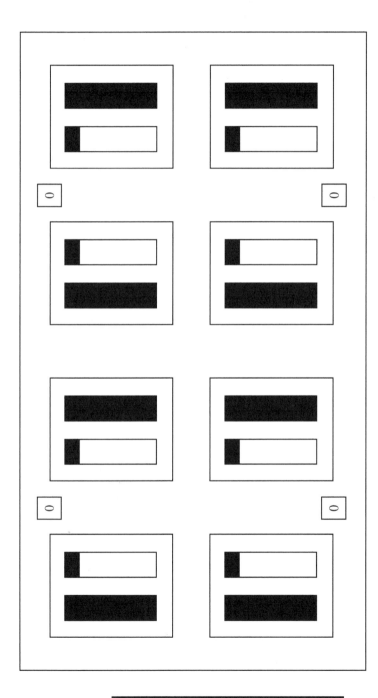

Figure 4.10 Floor Flip-Flop

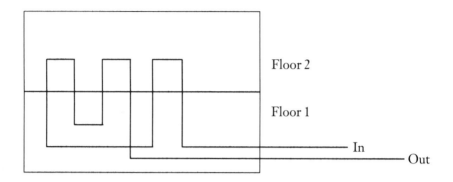

Figure 4.11   Poor Facility Flow

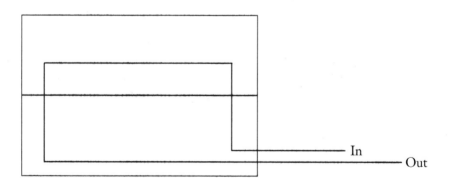

Figure 4.12   Improved Facility Flow

LOT-SIZE REDUCTION

The lot-size reduction team includes members from production and production control. The team's goal is to continuously reduce lot sizes delivered to the line and worked on by the line. The ultimate goal of JIT manufacturing lot-size reduction is one-piece-per-operator at any one time. The minimization of lot sizes throughout the manufacturing process reduces cycle time, ending inventory, quality exposures, and maximizes completed units per day.

Most manufacturing floors are flooded with inventory. A simple assessment can be made of a company's material control capability by looking for stacks of inventory on or near the manufacturing floor.

The lot-size reduction team has the responsibility of examining line balance problems as they continuously reduce lot sizes from thousands, to hundreds, to tens, to ones. This is a difficult task because manufacturing lines must be reconfigured constantly, and different configurations require different flow designs, space, tooling, and fixturing, and a different number of people.

ORGANIZING AND CLEANING THE WORKPLACE

There is no mystery to organizing and cleaning the workplace. There is nothing worse than going to work in a dingy, dirty environment where management is too cheap to spend the money needed to provide workers with a healthy and safe atmosphere. Excuses for lack of maintenance, lighting, and dirt went out with nineteenth century management. This includes organizations in the so-called "third world" countries. If one company in Southeast Asia can offer a clean, safe environment, so can the rest.

Tools, fixtures, and direct and indirect materials should be stored, shelved, and organized so they do not clutter work areas. Space must be left to do this, shelves constructed, and racks built. Whatever team requirements are established, organization should never again be allowed to become disruptive and dangerous.

Many teams that struggle with the idea of cleanliness have

problems. Everyone has a different definition and perception for what "clean" means. The team should define cleanliness as clearly as possible. One team defined "sidewalk cleanliness" as "no foreign materials, movable or permanent, should be visible with the naked eye from a height of five feet." Obviously this covers cigarette butts, papers, stains, even small piles of windblown sand.

Cleanliness does not mean that office desks can remain cluttered, trash cans overflowing, or books in disarray. Every area of the facility should be covered by requirements, inside and out, hallways, offices, and bathrooms. The message of cleanliness should be clearly communicated to all employees. Individuals should be made responsible for maintenance of standards in their immediate work area.

There should not be any confusion regarding cleanliness and organization. Although a person is responsible for the immediate and surrounding work area, management has the task of assuring that common areas are controlled and clean. Lighting above operators' heads, flooring, hallways, walls, ceilings, rungs under tables, stairways, bathrooms, patios, and other common areas must be maintained diligently.

KANBAN AND KANBAN SYSTEMS

KANBAN often is referred to as the *pull system*. The original meaning was associated with a marked location that, when empty, should be filled or at least signaled for an operation to begin. This marked location is known as the KANBAN or KANBAN square.

The idea is that parts are pulled from point A to point B rather than pushed, as in conventional manufacturing. An ideal system would see parts pulled from the marketplace, through an original equipment manufacturer (OEM) and its distributor network, through vendors, all the way to raw material suppliers. In this most general view, materials are pulled from company to company as higher level assemblies are built. Thus, the need for high-quality, dock-to-stock deliveries in small lot sizes in a just-in-time manner.

The miniature version of the KANBAN is between operators on a manufacturing line. Simply put, an operator cannot build product unless the next operator in line has "pulled" product from a marked location between the two operations. Material is literally pulled through value-adding operations, out to final packing, and across the loading dock into shipping containers. Every operation depends on the operation following it in line. The "marked" operation is known as the KANBAN and is as simple as a taped square on a table-top to a pallet on a loading dock.

The KANBAN is a reversal from most manufacturing material flow strategies currently being used. Most existing strategies push materials. The conceptual difference between conventional push systems and the KANBAN pull system is part of what makes the implementation of KANBAN extremely difficult. KANBAN, however, is a backbone of TQC/JIT and is a significant tool.

More excuses can be found to not put a KANBAN in place or to remove a KANBAN than any other aspect of TQC/JIT.

Beware! The quality problems, inefficiencies, imbalances, excess inventory, and all the many problems that can be normally hidden in a traditional manufacturing line become rapidly visible with KANBAN. There will be extreme effort to sabotage KANBAN. KANBAN means work that separates those who can solve problems from those who cannot solve problems.

Manufacturing lines will run in a herky-jerky manner. Many operators will appear to have no work to do — an indication of line imbalance. Inexperienced operator teams tend to be more out of balance than experienced teams.

The team selected to implement KANBAN must be aware of the problems inherent in implementation. This team must have the ability to make rapid adjustments in the operation of the line, to recognize symptoms, and be free to take action to improve the flow. The team would do well to set objectives that focus on one JIT line at a time, perhaps using the pilot line (recommended earlier in this chapter) for initial implementation and observation.

The KANBAN CAT will need strong top-level management support due to the probable production losses that will occur in the early stages. These losses will be more than made up for in a short time.

KANBAN measurement should follow the suggestions provided in Chapter 1, Figure 1.6. Cycle times, hours per unit, scrap, defect, completed assemblies, and ending inventory data should be collected daily and plotted for the team to see. FIT activities should focus on this monitoring data to select problems that may be solved by working alone or with other specialized teams such as suggested in this chapter.

LINE STOP

The line stop team has the job of implementing procedures that dictate when a manufacturing line should and will be stopped by a team member or lead. An increase in quality defects is the reason to stop a line.

Now, there are bound to be some misinterpretations concerning line stop. For those who have never stopped or seen a manufacturing line stopped, rest assured that there are plenty of reasons to stop one.

The line should not be stopped for quality problems that are ongoing and within control limits. Such problems should become the focus of FIT activities as part of the continuous improvement process.

The line should be stopped for major catastrophic happenings that greatly increase the proportion of defective product coming from the line. The manufacturing line also should be stopped for any condition that shows a trend toward or a point indicating an out-of-control condition on a control chart.

Immediate action should be taken to remove the cause of the problem from the line. Preventive action should follow any line stop that has had the cause removed from the line. In many cases, the reason for one line to stop exists undetected in other lines manufacturing similar products. These actions are the responsibility of the line stop team. Production and quality people usually make up the members of the line stop team. Again, line stop procedures and guidelines can be tested on the pilot line prior to implementation across the manufacturing floor.

STATISTICAL PROCESS CONTROL

The topic of statistical process control (SPC) is infinite and complex.[19] Many books are written on the topic, but a few simple suggestions are presented here.

Each manufacturing JIT line should have at least one P-chart at its end to record and display the proportion of defective product being manufactured. This can be part of the FIT monitoring activities. The reasons for rejects should be coded and analyzed using Pareto analysis, and also used for FIT discussion.

Critical parameters (those dimensions or attributes that will absolutely cause the product to fail at the customer's or in the next process step) should then be sampled. Mean and range control charts should be established and maintained. That is, each critical parameter should have its own control chart maintained, with uniformly sized samples, at regular intervals. This critical parameter data also can form the basis for process information which should be delivered to customers as part of their occasional or ongoing inquiry into how process control is maintained.

Next, the SPC team should be loaded with personnel from production and quality who are familiar with not only control chart SPC techniques, but with experimental research design and data analysis as well. This team will, in an effort to support various FITs, help design experiments, collect and analyze data, and help draw objective conclusions regarding the outcome of the experiment.

The SPC team members also should be part of an ongoing training effort to familiarize all organizational personnel, manufacturing or not, with basic SPC techniques and interpretation.

The SPC team should then centralize the basic data from each line, help to visually display this data so that other teams may quickly see results (e.g., the line stop and visual signals teams), and design some way to summarize the information for higher management review.

Note: The data are to be used by teams to manage the line. The data are only secondarily summarized for management review. Most organizations have these priorities backward.

The SPC team is responsible for establishing a system to measure, record, and display process capability (Cpk) information. Process capability summaries should be available for all FITs as potential problem areas. Figure 4.13 is a Korean example of a process capability report. There are many software packages currently available that allow for quick and easy capability reporting.

Figure 4.13 shows a distribution that has drifted to the high side of the specification limits (USL = Upper Specification Limit, LSL = Lower Specification Limit). The chart shows that some proportion of the product is being made which falls outside of the USL. The resulting capability index (Cpk) is .62. This is considered low. A rule of thumb for process capability acceptance is that Cpk should equal or exceed 1.33. Even a Cpk of 1.33, however, can use improvement and a team should not stop at 1.33 thinking the job has been completed. A Cpk of 1.33 is minimum!

A strong CAT emphasis should be placed on process capability improvement. Figure 4.14 illustrates a Korean CAT plan to improve the process capability problem shown in Figure 4.13. The plan was put into action and results tracked on Figure 4.15. That figure shows a good downward trend in scrap due to out-of-specification manufacturing. The chart shows a defect code (172, 171, etc.) breakdown by using hatching and shading in a bar-graph format. The meaning of each defect code is not important here as they are used only for illustration purposes. This represents a good process capability improvement. Cpk is a key indicator that will show great yield improvement if managed correctly.

CAPABILITY REPORT

Date: 03-23-1988

Plant/Dept	Part Name/Number	Eqpt or Operation
IKL/Q.C.	Susp Ass'y/510360	Gram Machine (New Die)
Characteristic	Engineering Specifications	IKL
Mechanical	8.90 to 10.90	Gram Load

PROCESS CAPABILITY PARAMETERS

Sample Size	120	Specification Limits	8.90 to 10.90	
Mean	10.3292	% Below LSL	0	Lower Z = 4.69
Standard Deviation	.3047	% Above USL	3.07	Upper Z = 1.87
Skewness	.225	Capability: Cpk = .62	CP ratio = 91.4%	CP index = 1.09
Kurtosis	− .533	Distribution Type	Normal	
3-Sigma Limits	9.4151 to 11.2433	4-Sigma Limits	9.1104 to 11.548	

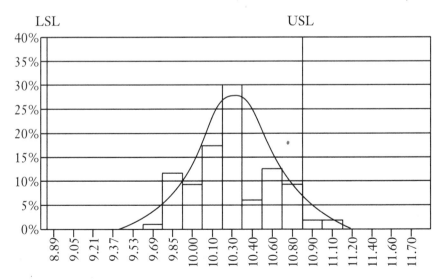

Figure 4.13   Process Capability Example

C.A.T. #8 ACTIVITY

Distribution:
   IKL – Y.I. Lee/K.W. Park/C.M. Han/H. Hwang
         K.S. Kim/B.S. Choi/P.H. Bong/B.K. Sung/S.H. Han
   IMC – Q.I.T.

Leader	S.J. Kim (Q.C.)		Member:	G.I. Shin (Prod),		
Objective:	In Process Scrap For Type Susp. Ass'y (except D.M.R. & Salvage)					

Code	Objective	Player	July 27 28 29 30	Aug 31 32 33 34	Sep 35 36 37 38 39
1.0	Organize C.A.T.	Q.I.T.	xx		
2.0	Monitoring	S.J. Kim		xx - -	xx - -
3.0	Analysis				
3.1	Process review	All		xx xx xx xx	xx xx xx xx x) - - - - - - - - - - - - - - - - - -
3.2	Cause analysis	All			
4.0	Corrective action				
4.1	Planning corrective action	All			
4.2	Setting reduction plan				
4.3	Taking corrective action				x)
4.3.1	Change process fixture				
4.3.1.1	Fabricate new fixture & evaluation	J.H.Park/ S.J. Kim			
4.3.1.2	Increase TTL number of new fixture	J.H. Park/ J.K. Lee			
4.3.2	Operator training by using monitor results	G.I. Shin		xx - -	xx - -

Note: - - Plan,   xxxx Actual,   ) Completion and/or Revised Plan

Figure 4.14   Korean CAT Plan

C.A.T. #8 ACTIVITY (continued)

Date: Apr. 11, 88   Rev: 02
Prepared by: S. J. Kim
Reviewed by: S. H. Han

J.K. Lee/J.H. Kwon (Engr)			Quarter:				
			Goal:				
			Status:				
Oct	Nov	Dec '87	Jan '88	Feb	Mar	Apr	May
40 41 42 43	44 45 46 47	48 49 50 51 52	1 2 3 4	5 6 7 8	9 10 11 12 13	14 15 16 17	18 19 20 21

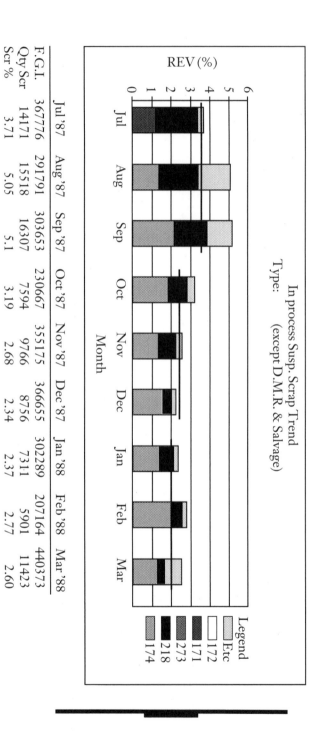

Figure 4.15   Corrective Action Team Results

Trend charts may be used to show financial figures. In previous chapters and in Chapter 5, cost figures are presented that may easily be plotted on trend charts. This task is important to cost monitoring and savings efforts.

VISUAL SIGNALS (ANDON)

The ANDON team is responsible for planning and implementing a technique for quickly and visually showing the status of a line. This can be done in many ways. Some companies use flashing lights to show out-of-control quality conditions, material shortages, or other problems. Visual displays are also used to show material locations and routings and are often integral components in pull systems.

One company set up a color system for displaying quality manufacturing levels (Figure 4.16, example from Korea). Based on SPC charts, red meant an out-of-control condition and signalled that the line should be stopped. Yellow meant the trend was in control, but operating at an excessive reject level. Yellow was a signal to managers and higher-level FITs that barriers were in existence. Yellow signals were the responsibility of management. A green sticker meant that the chart was showing an in-control condition at low reject levels. Red, yellow, and green stickers were placed on a master wall chart which then showed status of each operation in every line.

The stickers were accompanied by red flags. Any line or part of a line in a red sticker condition had a hard plastic red flag placed on the line to indicate that a problem existed. This flag (cheaper than lights, bells, and whistles, but not as capable of attracting quick attention) then acted as the visual signal for a corrective action team to get to work.

TRAINING (CERTIFICATION)

For companies without formal training programs, a training team is mandatory. For those with formal training, the team can act in at least

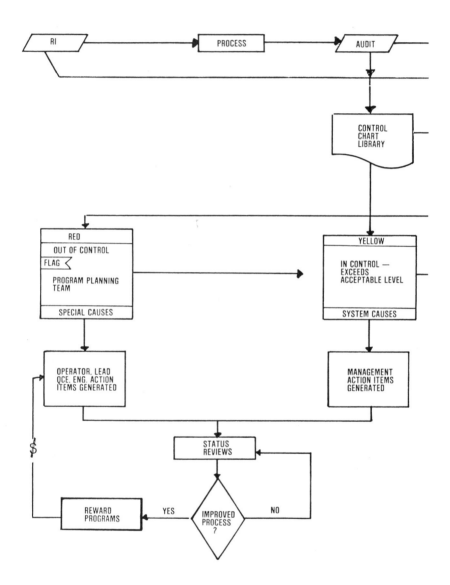

Figure 4.16   ANDON

(Figure 4.16 continued)

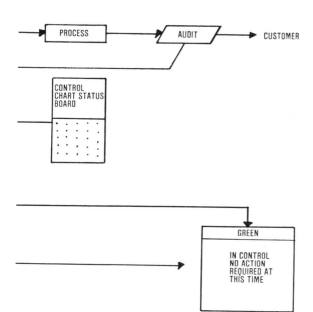

an advisory capacity to the established training function. The importance of cross training and cross certification, system training, was discussed in Chapter 3.

Based on training needs identified by the training team, a complete curriculum must be established that reflects the training needs of all members in the organization. The curriculum consists of at least an outline of all courses required by each group and an outline of what should be taught in each course. Each course should have a stated objective and some way of objectively determining whether or not the students of the course have attained the intended objective.

Many training efforts have been observed which focus evaluation efforts on how the students "liked" the materials, teacher, or the room. Such information is subjective and will do little to improve training. The only serious question to be asked is: Can the students successfully implement what they learned? If this question cannot be answered or is answered with a "no," the training program is a failure.

The curriculum, the trainers, training materials, and even the classroom should become a part of the ongoing TQC/JIT effort of continuous improvement.

A training manager or coordinator usually is required, depending on the size of the organization and the anticipated growth rate.

Different companies handle training in different ways. Usually, a blend of outside specialists and inside experts is organized and scheduled in a way that fulfills curriculum requirements.

Again, the function of the training team is to identify training problems, priorities, analyze, and set corrective action in motion, usually through or in conjunction with the formal training organization.

SETUP TIME REDUCTION

Most companies have some problems with the amount of time it takes to set up tooling, fixturing, or machinery when jobs are switched from one configuration to another. The goal of the setup time reduction team is to locate all such problem areas in the plant and to find ways to minimize the setup time.

It is not unusual to walk into a machine shop and find that 50 percent of all staff-hours are expended in setup.

Often, setup time is a function of how ready small tools, materials, etc., are for the actual changeover. If an operator or engineer has to run around a shop looking for a screwdriver, then for a pair of pliers, then for a different screwdriver, it is easy to see how time is lost. Tool kits can be made up and made available before the changeover is scheduled to take place. Changeover kits can save a lot of time.

Changeover kits, however, are only one solution. Many mechanical changes can be made to fixtures which allow quick breakdown and setup. Programs can be written ahead of time and in a generic format for reducing setup times on automated computer-controlled machines.

The team selected from production, engineering, and quality has a long-term task of measuring setup times, looking at causes, and coming up with corrective action efforts to reduce these times.

AUTOMATION REVIEW

Earlier it was mentioned that the long-term objective of JIT is to fully automate a line. It also was stated that due to today's level of certain technologies and the costs associated with these technologies, automation was not a realistic current goal. Nevertheless, the goal is to produce a fast-flowing, error-free manufacturing line.

The automation review team has the task of continuously reviewing available machinery and equipment which can be cost-effectively linked together to replace human contact with manufacturing. As lot sizes are reduced to a single unit, a natural flow has developed which is similar to what a simple machine can handle.

The team's responsibility is to study the operator's motions and activities in an effort to identify or design, purchase or build a machine that will further reduce product variability and improve throughput.

CYCLE-TIME CONTROL

A cycle-time control team continuously monitors each JIT line's cycle times and searches for ways to reduce cycle times. It was stated earlier that cycle times are most often a function of lot sizes. This team, however, must look for ways beyond lot-size reduction to improve cycle times.

Often, the line-stop specifications will have the effect of increasing rather than lowering cycle times. When lines stop, cycle times increase. This means the cycle-time team may get involved in helping search out a new vendor for a part which consistently causes line stops.

The cycle-time team not only looks for ways to reduce cycle times, but also tries to find reasons and solutions for cycle times that fluctuate greatly within a given line. For instance, part number changes often will cause cycle times to go out of control (yes, cycle times can be plotted on a control chart, complete with an average and control limits). The team might decide to tackle this problem.

SUMMARY

Chapter 4 is an attempt to disclose some common team approaches and stimulate thought for developing new team approaches. First, special teams are required to support the overall implementation and continuous improvement effort required by a TQC/JIT system. Second, the list of special teams described herein is by no means exhaustive.

For instance, Figure 4.18 (example from the United States) shows a hockey-stick delivery schedule. The striped bars on the chart represent planned shipments, the solid black bars represent actual shipments. The chart shows a monthly increase in planning and production within each quarter (April-June, July-September, October-December) followed by a sharp dropoff during the first month of each following quarter. This represents severe instability for manufacturing, not to mention the rest of the

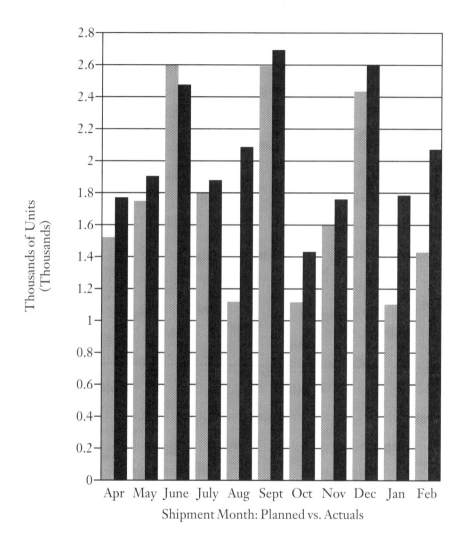

Figure 4.18   Hockey-Stick Planning

company. Nothing dreamt up by mankind could be more destructive to TQC/JIT efforts than a schedule with such ups and downs. A suggestion would be to form a team comprised of members from production, purchasing, sales, and production control whose job would be to smooth out this monster.

An order entry team is certainly within the scope of our perspective of application of JIT time-saving techniques to nonmanufacturing areas. Order entry can be one of the biggest bottlenecks in a company drastically in need of line balance and linearity in order to ensure rapid customer response.

New product development can often use a dose of the same medicine.

Although this chapter has focused on specialized techniques and teams most commonly applied to manufacturing settings, there are numerous other examples and discussions throughout this book to inspire creative thought toward the application of these ideas to nonmanufacturing areas.

Chapter 5 focuses on several methods for gathering, displaying, and prioritizing costs for the purpose of corrective action.

5

Keeping a Focus On Cost Savings

*T*he main reason for implementing a continuous improvement program is to help an organization achieve and maintain profitability. By reducing errors and speeding throughput of products and services, the organization becomes increasingly capable of competing successfully.

Throughout previous chapters, teams have been urged to apply TQC/JIT principles to the solution of problems. The urging has repeatedly been to reduce rejects and throughput time as a means of saving money. It also has been pointed out that in many cases, teams can collect and display cost variables (rather than defect or time variables) with the intent of improvement. Throughout the first few chapters, few examples for cost analysis have been illustrated. However, limitless opportunities exist for nonfinancial team members to understand and apply simple cost ideas to corrective action efforts.

WHERE ARE THE COSTS?

For manufacturing organizations, costs seem to begin before materials are brought into the factory.[17] Shipping, handling, holding and storage costs accumulate. As materials move through various operations, costs accumulate in terms of the people paid for the hours they spend building the product in addition to nonvalue-adding overhead activities such as engineering, quality, leads, supervisors, inspectors, payroll, document control, production control, test, rework, re-inspection and retest, clerks, maintenance, machine shop personnel who support tooling and fixturing, systems analysts and programmers, telephone and fax operators, secretaries, design engineers, draftspersons, guards, shipping and receiving personnel and other people who are needed to keep the organization moving. Costs continue to be added throughout the company; each department makes mistakes that cost even more money because work is delayed and must be redone, whether internally or because of customer returns. These categories of avoidable and reducible costs provide some targets for TQC/JIT improvements. Such costs exist in all functions, are identifiable, and are reducible.

Combine this with the facility costs, the building, electricity, water, power, air compressors, heaters, air conditioners, clean rooms, tables, chairs, computers, telephone systems, file cabinets, cleaning, conference tables, etc., and you end up with significant overhead which indirectly supports manufacturing. These cost categories also are most certainly inflated due to rework and bottlenecks. The natural tendency of an organization with 30 percent rework is to take care of that rework by adding more people who require more space, tables, desks, tools, insurance, etc.

How many managers do you know who complain they cannot get the job done with the people they have who also have high rework demands. They would be happy to implement TQC/JIT if only management would give them more people (they have more important things to do — like rework). The purchasing department described in Chapter 3 serves as a good example of a department bloated in such a manner. The annual savings they realized from one small project was enough to reduce their staff (workspace, etc.) requirements by one person. Take that one person and assign different and new tasks and you have a department which can allocate one person to new projects and begin to dig its way out of the mud in which it has buried itself for years.

It seems that cost analysis has been a rather elusive subject for most nonfinancial types. This is especially true in the quality profession where costs classically are broken down into four main categories which have nothing to do with standard accounting practices. Quality publications generally like to discuss *prevention, internal and external failures,* and *appraisal* cost categories. These terms are alien to financial people, indeed, alien to most quality personnel. As a result, most organizational financial groups cannot comprehend what is needed, nor, it seems, do they desire to take the time to try to understand what is needed. Add this to the fact that quality professionals generally do not understand financial statements and the problem is compounded.

Trying to get quality cost analysis assistance from a financial group is next to impossible. Therefore, this chapter attempts to provide some reasonably simple alternatives for nonfinancial persons who are interested in collecting cost estimate data with the intent of reducing unnecessary costs.

REVIEW OF COST IDEAS

Quality professionals and publications like to break down costs into the categories shown as Table 5.1

Table 5.1   Traditional Quality Cost Categories

I. Prevention
   Design reviews
   Training
   Statistical process control
   Planning
   Management teamwork
   Preventive action
   Vendor control
   Customer interface
   Organization
   Attitude development

II. Internal Failures
   Rework
   Scrap
   Touchup

III. Appraisal
   Inspection
   Test
   Screening

IV. External Failures
   Customer returns
   Lost business
   Freight costs
   Reduced inventory turns

The list in Table 5.1 is not exhaustive. *The Principles of Quality Costs*, published by the American Society for Quality Control, breaks the list down into infinitely more detail.[6] The classifications are useful because they help us to understand where money can be lost, at least from the quality perspective. Again, the problem is a lack of financial department support for collection, analysis, and reporting of such costs.

The concept of prevention was discussed in Chapter 2. Prevention is the backbone of TQC/JIT. In most organizations, little time and effort are expended on preventing problems since fire fighting and corrective action consume most peoples' time and efforts.

If it were humanly possible to track all man-hours, expenses, supplies, lighting, and maintenance costs for activities that are considered preventive in nature, an organizational number would be developed which could be used to calculate what percent of the overall quality costs were spent on prevention. The percent of funds an organization spends on preventing problems, compared to finding and fixing them later (internal failures, appraisal, and external failures), is considered an indication of the organization's quality health. The more spent on prevention, the less spent overall. Many companies spend small amounts on prevention (see Chapter 3's barrier analysis example where operators have almost no training, but many perceived problems).

It is argued that the compilation of preventive (and other) costs is possible if standard costs are used. The term *standard costs* refers to general, estimated costs. Standard costs as described here means to collect data that shows staff-hours spent doing a job and multiplying this figure by the burdened labor rate(s) for the particular job classification. The purchasing example in Chapter 3 used standard costs to show financial losses and savings. The use of standard costs eliminates the need to specifically track all actual costs. Tracking actual costs is extremely expensive and, except for the legal requirements of running a company, it doesn't help management much.

The idea of using standard costs is advocated in this chapter. Any quality cost analysis is intended to do two or three things. The first purpose of cost analysis is to help teams set priorities in the same manner of Pareto, cycle time, and cause-and-effect analyses. The second purpose is to determine the relative (not exact to the penny) effects of corrective action. A third reason is to be able to report generalized cost savings, if they occur, to higher-level management.

Quality cost analysis should never appear in a financial report, financial statement, balance sheet, or annual report. This might happen 50 years from now, but even if required in such reports, such data would do little to help guide lower-level teams in their pursuit of continuous improvement. Therefore, actual costs are not mandatory.

Internal failure costs (Table 5.1) refer to all those activities that must be accomplished within the walls of an organization as a result of some activity not being done correctly the first time. Internal failure costs generally are high in companies and are the second major reason for going to a TQC/JIT system that emphasizes first-time quality.

Appraisal costs are the easiest to understand. Appraisal in this sense means to "judge the quality of" (Webster's New World Dictionary of the American Language), not to judge the monetary value of something.[24] Used this way, appraisal involves inspection, re-inspection, test, retest, screening and rescreening, and should include all costs associated with these activities. Such costs include not only man-hours but also equipment, facility, and other costs. A quick check can be done by examining a manufacturing floor, counting the inspectors, testers, and screeners, and dividing this total by the total number of direct labor personnel. Now you will have an idea of the proportion of costs associated with appraisal.

Interestingly, some companies evaluate prospective vendors with simple appraisal numbers. A customer may request the number of direct labor personnel in a facility and also ask for the number of people with "quality" titles (engineers, inspectors, test personnel, etc.). A quick division then tells the evaluation team where a facility stands. Generally, a customer using this evaluation technique is looking for vendors with less than 10 percent of its work force dedicated to inspection, screening, and test. Higher figures indicate lack of process control.

External failures comprise the most devastating costs. Once the customer becomes the recipient of poor products or services, the company's reputation has taken a big hit. One rude salesperson can mean a customer lost forever. One late shipment that fails in a customer's manufacturing line can mean a cancelled order. If there was ever a reason to protect the customer from bad quality, it is that external failure costs are the most expensive costs a company must bear. External failure costs must be minimized because recovery from their effects is extremely difficult.

This chapter specifically discusses how to collect and analyze some of these costs, but will not attempt to follow the Table 5.1 classification too closely. Reports that can result from compilations of such figures are interesting for management, but unless details are available for FIT and CAT activities, such reports are not immediately useful for corrective action. Costs that can be identified on a more local, team level do not necessarily have to be part of organizationwide cost data collection

From Table 5.1, the most expensive costs tend to be those outside of the organization, the external failures. There is no known method for measuring lost business costs, but some research has been done in this field.[8]

In October 1988, Spencer Hutchens, Jr., senior vice president of Intertek Services Corporation and president of the American Society for Quality Control gave a presentation at the National Quality Forum IV. His paper, "What Customers Want: Results of ASQC/Gallup Survey," was based on survey information and some extrapolation. Hutchens estimates that consumers lose about $5.5 billion dollars annually from having to throw away defective product and expenses related to returning product due to poor quality. If consumers are spending that much annually, and only an estimated 50 percent of the consumers even contacted a company regarding poor quality, imagine what the real cost must be to consumers, not to mention producers.

Another interesting classification system is emerging in professional quality circles. Two classifications of costs are proposed. First, *operating impact costs*, or costs that basically follow the points outlined in Table 5.1. Second, the *costs of ownership* concept is beginning to achieve some prominence. Costs of ownership refers to the idea that if my company receives product from your company, and my company has to inspect and screen parts you shipped, my company is paying to do what your company should have done in the first place. In other words, it costs my company money to "own" your product. The same applies to a consumer who has to have a television repaired after the warranty runs out. It is hypothesized that these costs should be added to the product's cost to determine the true cost.

Taken to a more specific step, if one operator in a manufacturing line must inspect and rework product from a previous operator, the receiving operator's costs are higher. The concept is applicable throughout the organization. In Chapter 3, error-loaded purchase requisitions received by the purchasing department increased their cost of ownership to the tune of one full-time employee. So, the between-departments costs concept holds up in addition to the between-companies or between-individuals costs.

Many companies are beginning to evaluate their vendors based solely on cost of ownership figures. The vendor with the lowest cost of ownership at a customer's is the vendor most likely to receive future orders and a spot on the preferred vendor list. At least one Hewlett-Packard plant reportedly has been selecting vendors to "cost of ownership" figures, and it is easy to understand why.

No debate is intended here. Both classifications make sense, both have some use, indeed, both are similar.

ANALYZING MANUFACTURING REWORK AND SCRAP COSTS

With a broad understanding of where costs are, some approach may be made to measuring and reporting costs in preparation for prioritization for improvement. In most manufacturing operations, measurement of quality costs is a dream quality professionals have. Most companies don't seem to have the time or resources to commit to collecting quality cost data or, in other facilities, someone in management has decided that such data is too sensitive and should not be in the public domain. Sometimes, there is simply no tool available to measure and report this data.

Many organizations have large centralized computer systems used for a variety of tasks. Often, the status that quality takes in an organization can be quickly determined by asking what priority quality requirements have on the computer. Within companies which have a centralized computer, most departments are asked what programming they need done in order to fulfill their reporting requirements. The quality department usually can expect limited, if any, support.

The computer becomes like a big printing machine, printing miles and piles of reports which are not that meaningful to users. An amazing thing about computers is that they can be used to generate more reports than the actual amount of data entered in the beginning. With one page of data, a programmer can, and often does, print out 50 pages of analysis. This is no joke.

Under such demand for computer time, quality reports are normally given a low number on the list of the year's priorities. This sad fact is reflected even in the list of priorities and available software sold as management packages. Management software packages usually are advertised to include "modules" such as accounting, payroll, production control, inventory control, order entry, purchasing, etc., which a company may continuously add to the system until all modules are tied together, interdependent, using each other's data. In these systems, bill of materials information and item master information forms the basis for many of the modules which automatically show material shortages and averages designed to help planners do their jobs of loading the factory, building product, and shipping product to customers.

Unfortunately, these systems rarely consider (and their designers have not historically considered) quality costs important enough to include as a module. Therefore, the quality engineer or team members trying to prioritize problems are left without central assistance in their quest for information.

It is suggested that another special, short-term team be established to develop a computerized system capable of collecting, analyzing, and reporting rework and scrap quality costs. As will be shown, a locally developed and utilized cost analysis system can be established which gives measurement power independent of centralized data processing. Furthermore, this system can be developed on a single personal computer or expanded into a network of personal computers using commonly available off-the-shelf software packages tied together with simple files and a data base manager. Such systems are now operational in Korea, Thailand, and the United States. The networked, PC-based, quality cost system is flexible enough to allow additional PCs to be added when needed and is useful for conventional and JIT manufacturing lines. This flexibility is important for any company going from traditional manufacturing into a TQC/JIT approach. Quite simply, the computer and its software can be set up to collect, crunch, and report throughout the transition from traditional manufacturing flows across time as JIT manufacturing flows are developed.

If any process flow is analyzed as a series of operations, each operation can be identified and the percent of completion of the product or service can be calculated. By the time a product or service is complete, 100 percent of its value has been added. This concept is illustrated in Figure 5.1 which shows a product manufacturing flow by work center (w/c) and, below each box, is shown the percent of completion added as the product is assembled. The percent of completion figure may be developed by looking at how much time is required by each operation and using the hours per unit figure or units per hour figure to calculate the percent of completion. This information generally is available from engineering and has been previously discussed in Chapter 3 as a method for performing cycle time analysis. For the product shown in Figure 5.1, a head gimbal assembly (HGA) was being assembled for later addition to a hard disk

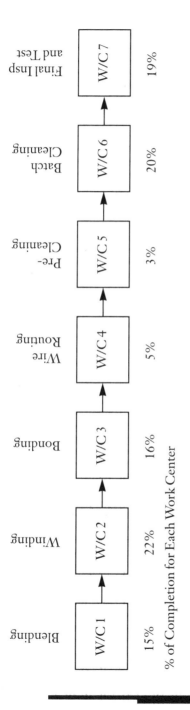

Process Flow

Blending	Winding	Bonding	Wire Routing	Pre-Cleaning	Batch Cleaning	Final Insp and Test
W/C 1	W/C 2	W/C 3	W/C 4	W/C 5	W/C 6	W/C 7
15%	22%	16%	5%	3%	20%	19%

% of Completion for Each Work Center

Figure 5.1 Product Manufacturing Flow

drive. HGAs are flying electromagnetic read/write heads used to encode bits of data onto hard disks (example from Korea). If the percentages below each box are added together, the total is 100 percent. In this case, coil winding which is done by hand under a 30x microscope takes 22 percent of the total assembly time while wire routing takes about 5 percent. These are not true numbers, but will serve our illustration purposes.

Using these "percent-of-completion" figures in a computer file establishes a basis for cost analysis. Again, many companies do not use percent-of-completion as a means of measuring efficiencies, but use hours-per-unit (HPUs) instead. Regardless, the first computer file which is required is either a percent-of-completion file or an HPU file.

Normally, a second file that is required by this idea also is available. This is simply a list of defect codes. Figure 5.2 is an example of such a list. As defects are discovered in the manufacture of a product, the written description of the defect is matched up with a number. The actual number used is irrelevant, but some logic in the assignment of classes of numbers to classes of defects should be used.

Now, a third file is required which uses information already compiled for the first two files. This is the rework flow file. An easy way to develop this file is to use the process flowchart (Figure 5.1) or to develop a process flowchart using typical flowchart symbols as discussed in Chapter 3. Using this flowchart, a single defect code could be evaluated.

The basic theory is that any time a defect is found that requires rework, the product (or partial product) must go back through certain routing which can be tracked. This routing adds cost to the product which is above the 100 percent figure illustrated in Figure 5.1. Any product or service that does not go through a line one time (the first time) with no rejects, must be rerouted through the line for rework. Any rework done to a product or service constitutes a cost above the 100 percent target and may be considered the cost of not doing the job correctly the first time.

MAJOR DEFECTS

1	Chip on ABS L/E
4	Chip on Zone 1
8	Chip on Non-ABS
9	Chip on Winding Window
11	Pit on Zone 1
18	Breakaway on Zone 1
25	Crack on Zone 1
35	Scratch on Zone 1
41	Center Rail Recession
45	Metal Mark (Scrap)
46	Metal Mark (RWK)
52	Contamination on ABS
59	Broken Slider Nose
62	Improper Glass Bonding at W/W
65	Undersized ETW
66	Oversized ETW
151	Removable Contam on Flexure
153	Removable Contam on Mtg Blk
161	Burned Welds on Flexure
162	Burned Welds on L/Beam, Arm
168	Rust on Flexure
174	Bent Flexure
182	Dent on Flexure
186	Dent on Gram Angle Formed Area
187	Dent on Mtg Block
194	Solid Burr on Flexure
198	Solid Burr on Mtg Block
201	Burn Through on Flexure
218	Dimple Separation (Scrap)
219	Dimple Separation (Rework)
431	Bare Wire (Rewinding)
438	Poor Tinning Condition
442	Bare Wire (U-Coating)
546	Split/Damaged Tube
602	Collapsed Coil Layer
603	Pinched Wire
604	Kinked Wire
605	Lint in Coil Layer
613	White Particle in Wind'g Area
614	Broken Wire
615	Contamination on Wire
620	Cold Tin
621	Untinned Wire

Figure 5.2   Defect Codes

Interestingly, cost targets in most companies include estimates for fallout or material scrap. What this says, in effect, is that companies plan for, allow, and therefore encourage some percent of their budgets to be spent for scrap. The message communicated throughout the company is that scrap is acceptable. In the context of TQC/JIT, scrap is not acceptable. The cost target should be for 100 percent yields. Everything above that cost target is money lost to the company. Money lost due to rework, scrap and wasted time comprise key targets for continuous improvement.

Let's consider an example. Figure 5.3 shows a rework route due to a defect called *inductance failure* which was found at a final quality audit gate. In order to rework the part for this defect code, the part had to go back to the DM (defective material) unit, be torn down, return through coil winding, through test, bonding, audit, route/crimp, tinning, pre-clean, batch clean, and into final quality again. Quite a rework! The burdened labor cost of the part was increased from the 100 percent target figure to about 185 percent, which is almost double the labor cost involved.

By calculating costs in a manner which shows an accumulation above the target cost, an estimated true cost of manufacturing (ETCOM) is obtained. For example, if the assembly discussed above cost $10 worth of labor to build with no rework, then the same unit would cost $18.50 worth of labor with an inductance failure. This is $8.50 above the target cost and also represents dollars subtracted from the profit margin.

An ETCOM system can be used to control processes, calculate the throughput costs for each customer, measure the dollar effect of tolerance changes on process capabilities, and to optimize manufacturing costs. Figure 5.4 is one type of product cost breakdown printout which shows failure costs, final product yields, and piece part yields by customer. Obviously, the higher "Failure Cost Per Quantity Entered" is a big hit for a manufacturer in spite of average yield figures. In this illustration, the "S" customer for whom lot "SE" was being built was showing an average cost above target of $.2920 per unit.

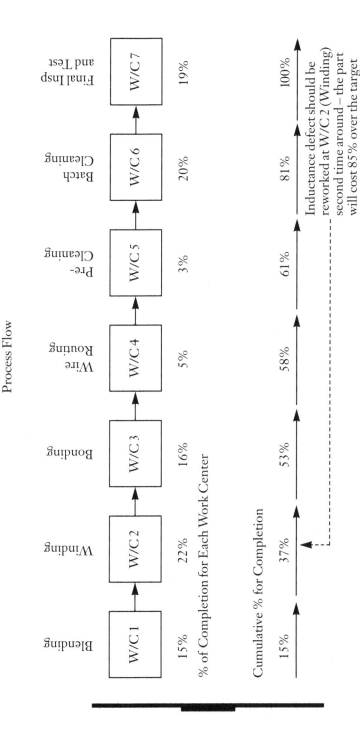

Process Flow

Blending	Winding	Bonding	Wire Routing	Pre-Cleaning	Batch Cleaning	Final Insp and Test
W/C 1	W/C 2	W/C 3	W/C 4	W/C 5	W/C 6	W/C 7
15%	22%	16%	5%	3%	20%	19%

% of Completion for Each Work Center

Cumulative % for Completion

| 15% | 37% | 53% | 58% | 61% | 81% | 100% |

Inductance defect should be reworked at W/C 2 (Winding) second time around – the part will cost 85% over the target cost of production, if part is scrapped – material cost will be added to the process cost to provide total failure cost.

Figure 5.3   Rework Route

Each defect code can be similarly analyzed. The result will be a third file which may be called "rework routings" or "failure routing file." This will take some time because of the overall number of defect codes that might exist or be required. In order to keep complications to a minimum, as the file is being built only one defect code at a time should be analyzed and rework route recorded.

Raw materials received by the factory are assigned a lot number for tracking through the manufacturing floor. Standard material prices also are entered along with part numbers and vendor codes. This allows tracking of scrap and accumulating part costs which can occur. For example, suppose a particular lot of parts is in the line which is later discovered to have a problem. These parts must be located, screened, reworked, etc. The costs will rapidly mount up and a *true* part cost will emerge. The true (cost of ownership) cost of a part is the original cost plus screening costs, rework costs, scrap costs, etc., due to vendor errors.

W. E. Deming discusses the implications of this system in *Quality, Productivity and Competitive Position*, Chapter 13.[25] In summary the formula $P < k1/k2$ is used to evaluate material costs where P is the average fraction defective in incoming lots of parts, $k1$ is the cost to inspect one part at receiving inspection, and $k2$ is the cost to completely rework, re-inspect, and retest an assembly that fails because a defective part was put into the production line. When $P < k1/k2$, no inspection of incoming materials is required. In-line costs for rework will be cheaper than 100 percent screening of received materials. The P value can be derived from either the vendor's final inspection (percent defective) or a customer's receiving inspection. The values for $k1$ and $k2$ come from the manufacturing quality cost system described here. Conversely, when $P > k1/k2$, 100 percent inspection of the incoming materials will be required to keep in-line failures and costs low. In other words, when the received percent defective is high, it is cheaper to screen at receiving inspection than to take a chance of dumping the materials into the line and having to screen and rework later.

Customer	Lot No.	Total Qty. Entered Process (Qty)	Total Failure Cost ($)	Failure Cost Per Qty. Entered ($)	Work/C. Compound Yield (%)	Slider Compound Yield (%)	Susp. Compound Yield (%)
A	AT *******	6,999	336	0.0480	94.94	99.70	99.70
C	CP *******	9,968	95	0.0095	97.42	99.80	99.60
M	MB *******	63,434	1,516	0.0239	90.04	98.80	99.20
M	MI *******	3,268	235	0.0719	76.93	97.22	98.71
M	MX *******	29,729	3,542	0.1191	90.82	97.82	99.40
PR	PR *******	43,421	4,040	0.0930	81.81	96.74	98.81
P	PT *******	22,925	2,255	0.0984	78.07	97.62	98.11
P	QE *******	31,975	7,368	0.2304	64.02	97.13	88.92
S	SE *******	345,056	70,058	0.2030	70.25	97.62	96.93
S	SU *******	27,093	7,910	0.2920	80.09	95.62	99.20
T	TD *******	99,168	16,767	0.1691	67.23	96.45	96.84
	_____	0	0	ERR	0.00	0.00	0.00
	_____	0	0	ERR	0.00	0.00	0.00

Figure 5.4   Product Cost Breakdown

There are a couple of more types of information this system will need. One is the *burdened labor rate*. The burdened labor rate is the average, per-hour, cost of direct (sometimes it includes indirect) labor in the plant. Someone should have this figure, even if they have not shared it. The second type of additional information which is required is the virgin cost of materials hitting the line. "Virgin" means that no one in your plant has added value to them yet.

In any facility with in-line inspection or audit, getting data into the system is an automatic offshoot of what is already established. A "lot record form" must be developed which allows auditors or inspectors to record, in a simple format, the number of rejects per lot for each defect code audited at that particular inspection gate. There is a different form for each inspection gate; each form calls out the main types of defects to be identified and eliminated at that point in the process. As inspectors do their job, they tally the number of defects of each type and record the tally on the form. The form is collected and passed to data input people, or entered into a terminal on the line. When enough of this type of data is input, a data base is established.

Figure 5.5 illustrates some examples of coding structures that can be used to store data. Shown are (A) sample material code structures, (B) rework/scrap code structure, and (C) the rework/scrap routing codes. The codes and order of subcodes that make up the codes are attempts to be logical, but are entirely up to the creator's whim.

Using a data base manager and with some programming, a report like that shown in Figure 5.6 could be published for teams or for successively higher levels of management. The left-hand column of Figure 5.6 shows the defect code and the defect description. Across the top of the chart is each operation as shown in the flowchart. Beneath the title of each operation are column headings which indicate the quantity ("Q'TY") and cost ($). The report shows, for each defect type, how many were found at each operation, and, based on the rework routings and burdened labor rate, how

Material Code Structures (A)

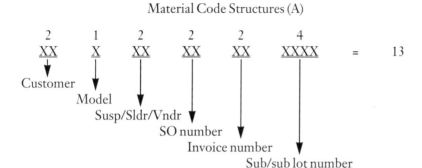

Rework/Scrap Code Structure (B)

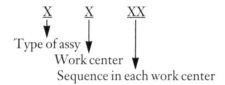

Rework/Scrap Routing Codes (C)

X   Std HPU
X   Std burdened labor costs

Defect code	Type	Route	Total HPU	Cost
1-40, 58-62	S	7F05 F1, M1	0.041	0.122
57	R	7F06 F1, M1, L2, L3, F1	0.238	0.713

Figure 5.5   Sample File Codes

***** Reject Status Report for all Work Center *****

Selection Criteria:

Major Defects	Blndg		Wind		P/cln		FQC		** Total **			
	Qty	Cost $	Qty	Cost $	Qty	Cost $	Qty	Cost $	Qty	(%)	Cost $	(%)
1 Chip on abs L/E	259	33.7	107	53.7	447	329.2	604	474.8	1,546	2.9	970.3	7.8
4 Chip on zone 1	10	1.3	98	50.0	194	140.9	1,341	1,048.9	1,699	3.2	1,284.2	10.3
8 Chip on non-abs	29	3.8	22	11.2	207	153.0	275	228.2	809	1.5	558.8	4.5
9 Chip wnd'g window	0	0.0	16	8.2	1	0.7	5	3.9	27	0.1	15.5	0.1
605 Lint in coil layer	0	0.0	6,152	123.0	2,521	367.8	865	138.4	9,655	18.2	637	5.1
902 Low inductance	0	0.0	145	55.1	0	0.0	6	3.5	151	0.3	58.6	0.5
912 No continuity	0	0.0	3	1.1	0	0.0	91	52.8	94	0.2	53.9	0.4
Miscellany	75	4.8	230	11.5	480	104.0	214	66.7	3,069	5.8	516.3	4.1
Total Qty	4,566		16,383		8,392		13,765		52,937	100		
Total Cost ($)		552		2,614		1,818		5,418			12,446	100

abbreviated format . . . exhibit only

Figure 5.6 Variation

much more than the 100 percent target, manufacturing spent to build the product. On the right-hand side of the report, the total quantity, percent, and cost for each defect code is accumulated. All costs and quantities are added across the chart to arrive at this total.

As an example, defect code number 1 (chip on abs L/E) showed 1,546 parts found defective (2.9 percent of the total defectives) with a cost of $970 (or 7.8 percent of the costs). This is an interesting point because, even though defect code 1 would not enjoy a high level of priority for corrective action based on a Pareto analysis, 7.8 percent of the quality cost dollars are being spent on this problem. The cost analysis has shown a different prioritization of problems than the quantity or percent analyses.

Another perspective may be taken with this data. Consider defect code 605 (Lint in Coil Layer). The only place that lint may be entrapped in the coil layers is during the winding process, but notice how many of these defects are found throughout other processes. Since this defect occurs in the first process step, it means that the product must go all the way back to the beginning for rework if the defect is not discovered until final quality inspection. The result is more than a 100 percent addition to the cost to manufacture the product! In the case of lint in the coil discovered in final quality inspection, the product must go through a complete tear down (with some resulting scrap) and a complete rebuild. A smart FIT team organized in the coil-winding operation of a JIT line could prevent a lot of these costs. Operator inspection could be initiated with a first time 100 percent acceptable product goal established. This one week report shows $637 spent on this type of rework (that's $33,124 per year). This defect represents 5.1 percent of the total internal failure costs. A three percent reduction (5.1% – 3.0% = 2.1% remaining) in this single defect would save the company almost $20,000 per year. If successful, this reduction would probably end up with greatly reduced inspection costs. If no product were to leave the area with lint in the coil, no inspectors or operators farther down the line would have to inspect for this defect. Although we realize that 100 percent inspection will not take out 100 percent of the defects, cost-reduction improvements are bound to be made.

The data can be used to establish inspection and corrective action points closer to the point of origin, thereby greatly reducing rework and scrap costs. It does not take a genius to know that catching defects close to the point of origin is cheaper than finding them after the final product is completed.

The bottom of the chart shows that each operation may be analyzed based on the total quantity and cost of rejects coming from the operation. This analysis tells us which operations are doing the best job and which are doing the worst.

Based on the rate of occurrence of the defect and the cumulative costs across operations, a cost-justifiable proposal can be written which will show which corrective action approach is going to help the company become more profitable. By studying the cost analysis, a production or manufacturing manager who has historically seen no use for a formal training program can target specific defect codes and costs which are attributable to workmanship errors as opposed to machine or tooling problems. A proposed training program based on training and learning curves could be installed.

Another use of such data is to discuss purchasing practices with buyers who buy only from the cheapest vendors. Considering a particular part number, why not look at the accumulated defect costs that are attributable to manufacturing or engineering buy offs of materials which do not meet specifications? Track these costs through the entire line, add these costs to the purchase price, and the result is the *actual* price of purchased piece parts (your ownership cost).

Engineering managers also can use this data to cost-analyze corrective actions which were previously thought unjustified.

There are a lot of uses for cost analysis data, which go far beyond the lower-level FIT team. The implications are for higher-level FITs and CATs to work on issues which can really save the company money. The system gives meaning to operationalizing "cost savings." Process problems pop out like warts. They are unsightly and not at all socially acceptable.

The system described establishes a data base which also can be used to develop control charts.[15] The accumulation of costs and counts of defects, by manufacturing operation and by manufacturing line is powerful. There are a number of good control chart software packages available which will allow the computer user to take data from the data base and quickly chart the results complete with control limit calculations.

Additionally, there are statistical analysis packages that can be tied into this personal-computer-based quality cost system. Exploratory data analysis using multiple regression or canonical correlation becomes a real possibility. Statistical comparisons between groups using t-tests or analysis of variance is also available and quickly executed as teams continue to question available data.[5]

The data base becomes extremely powerful (as illustrated in Figure 5.7) (example from an American company).[19] The idea depicted is simply that as data are collected from a manufacturing stream, with the correct computerized support, both general reporting and specific continuous improvement data needs can be met. In Figure 5.7, the "Umbrella" data base serves two requirements when management reporting is crunched out by a mainframe computer, but online terminals are used in conjunction with a statistical analysis software package to allow for in-depth exploration of the data in conjunction with corrective action and functional improvement team activities.

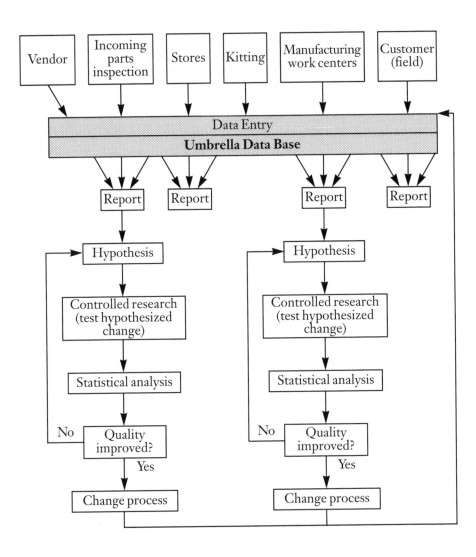

*Figure 5.*7

EXAMPLES OF NONMANUFACTURING COST ANALYSES

Material Requirements Planning (MRP) System

Suppose a company has a computer system that is used to control material purchasing, scheduling, shipments, builds, etc. Such a system is commonly called materials requirements planning (MRP).

In order to establish and maintain an accurate and timely materials accounting, several steps should be followed. First, the bill of materials must be set up by engineering and entered into the computer. The bill of materials (BOM) is simply an organized list of all pieces and parts to be used to build a product. This list is first generated by an engineer who knows the product and the pieces it takes to build it. The BOM also includes, along with the names of each piece part, the piece part number (assigned according to some system), and the number of pieces of like configuration which must go into the product. For instance, a toothbrush takes one handle (part number = 10023) and 500 bristles (part number 10024). So, the BOM for a toothbrush would have two items, with part numbers and quantities required.

Another part of the MRP system requires information to be input into the computer which carefully and in detail describes each piece part. This second input document is referred to as the item master. It is a master record of each item to be used in the final product.

Other aspects of the MRP system are used to control the materials data entry and inventory counts. In order to maintain an accurate system, somehow a record of how many of the materials stored and used must be updated as materials are used so that the system may subtract the used items from the quantity on hand thereby informing the material planner that more materials need to be ordered. There is more to the system than this, but the idea that materials are controlled administratively and that such administrative systems run into costly problems that can be handled by TQC/JIT strategies is apparent.

Suppose a company has such a system and that occasionally manufacturing lines cease to function because there are material shortages or the wrong materials were delivered to the factory, leaving the factory short of the correct materials. Another problem that could occur is that the final product fails to pass a particular test. Analysis of why the test was failed could reveal that the wrong part was being put into the assembly. Additionally, suppose a financial analyst was examining the company balance sheet and financial statements and calculated inventory turns to be 2.1. These are all symptoms of an MRP system that is having problems.

Figure 5.8 shows how errors can become compounded in an MRP (or any other) system.

	Operation				
	1 BOM	2 IM	3 Count	4 DE	Total system accuracy
Accuracy rate	.98	.97	.965	.95	.871

Figure 5.8   Compounding Errors in an MRP System

This figure shows that after analysis by a FIT, the bill of materials was found to be 98 percent accurate (only 2 percent error rate), the item master was 97 percent accurate, inventory count 96.5 percent accurate, and the data entry had only a 5 percent error rate. From the perspective of any one operation, the system appears to be in good shape. The problem is that as a system there was, overall, about a 13 percent (100 − 87.1 = 12.9 percent) error rate. The total system accuracy is calculated by multiplying each operation accuracy rate times the product of the previous operations' accuracy rates (.98 x .97 x .965 x .95 = .871). In other words, the system required almost 13 percent rework. At an average burdened labor rate of $23.50 per hour, with five people responsible for maintaining the system (five people, each working 170 hours per month @ $23.50/hour) the cost to find and correct errors was about $2600 per month. This figure, although derived directly from hours expended within a single function, represents only part of the total dollar losses.

FIT and CAT members would do well to consider costs that are not so easily observable. The symptoms stated above include line stops due to material shortages, incorrect parts in assemblies, and reduced inventory turns. The team should think of these added costs and attempt to implement simple standardized methods for capturing some of these losses. For example, by communicating with a higher level production FIT, a monitoring subsystem which captures operator downtime due to material shortages can be easily implemented. The cost chart monitored by the MRP FIT team could be either a combination of cost charts or a series of cost charts which each show dollar losses due to different symptoms. In other words, all costs could be combined into one chart or different charts for different causes could be maintained with corrective action focused on each specific cause.

Sales Order Entry

Sales orders generally enter an organization either through a direct customer telephone call or through a salesperson. Sales orders must be entered into the organizational system, sometimes entered into a computer, be approved and worked on by engineering, document control, purchasing, and material planning groups until, eventually, the sales order becomes part of a manufacturing plan. Many things can go wrong with sales order entry systems (Figure 5.9).

Some symptoms of problems include "lost" sales orders, and long delays in organizational response to customers who have placed sales orders. The question of "What is wrong?" usually is the result of customers calling up to complain that they have received no response to the sales order they placed six weeks ago. Rest assured, it is somewhere in the system, meaning a frantic search is launched to locate the missing paperwork.

This is a perfect CAT problem or at least a problem which can be addressed by several FITs working in harmony to clean up their part of the problem. The problem usually is approached from a JIT

Symptoms:
    A. Long delays in pushing S/Os through system.
    B. Lost orders.

Causes:
    A. Linear approval process.
    B. Bottlenecks at each step.
    C. S/O errors.

Solutions:
    A. Use JIT or network strategies to reduce cycle times.
    B. Look at manpower loading costs vs. estimated $ losses
       — justify balance.
    C. Use Pareto, Ishikawa, and control chart cost analyses to control.

Figure 5.9   Sales Order Entry

perspective with the emphasis on reducing the sales order cycle time.

The corrective action team should begin by flowcharting the process and performing a cycle time analysis. When such data are gathered, certain causes will emerge from the cause-and-effect analysis. Common causes for sales order delays include a high error or reject rate, bottlenecks at each step in the process, and a linear approval process (the sales order goes through one step at a time, each department waiting for the previous one to finish the job in a push system manner). Invariably, the sales order process will be found to have no stated requirements with regard to what is good and bad quality. Also, when requirements are finally agreed on and data collection begun, sales orders will be found at numerous points in the process to be 100 percent rejectable (similar to the purchase order sample used in Chapter 3).

This brings the team to the place where they must consider the costs of this mess. Obviously there is rework going on whether the sales order is being cleaned up at the end of the process or being sent back from one department to the previous one because it was wrong.

Cost data collection here is similar to that described for the purchasing group in Chapter 3, and similar to that described for the

MRP group. Standard burdened labor rates should be agreed on. Individuals involved in the rework process should log the time they spend inspecting and redoing work until some baseline estimates of the rework costs are collected on a weekly basis. The number of man-hours counted up for each sales order (here an average rework charge per sales order might be a good idea) should be accumulated and multiplied by the standard costs decided upon by the team. This baseline number should then be plotted on a weekly basis to be used to establish corrective action targets.

Other costs might be considered for the equation as well. Do customers cancel orders for which a company cannot respond to a sales order? Any cancellations due to organizational inability to respond should be considered as a cost. Such costs should include the hours already expended by various departments in an effort to complete the sales order.

Once a cost figure is plotted, JIT ideas should be used to attack and reduce cycle times. Costs by department should be analyzed using Pareto, cause-and-effect diagrams, and more specific cost-control charts. Cost-control charts are developed exactly like any other control chart, except the Y-axis is used to plot money values (dollars, yen, baht, pesos, etc.). As in the purchasing analysis, manpower loading in sales order systems generally is found to be beyond requirements due to excessive error and rework rates. This manpower loading cost should be compared to the estimated financial losses due to errors or delays. Corrective action targets should be to cut costs by reducing unnecessary manpower through subsystem improvements. As the sales order system smooths out, fewer people should be required for maintenance.

Document Control Errors

Losses due to documentation errors can be astronomical!

Engineers generally do not make drawing mistakes, but occasionally drawing revision levels are found which do not reflect current customer or vendor requirements. Another symptom of

Symptoms:
1. Your drawing REV levels do not match your customer and/or vendor drawing REV levels.
2. Large WIP or customer return hits which are easily tracked to DC errors.

Causes:
1. ECO delays (bottlenecks).
2. Missing link between purchasing/sales and vendor/customer.
3. Improper procedures, training, or . . . .

Solutions:
1. JIT or network ECO system.
2. Track rework/return $ losses due to spec errors.
3. At least quarterly customer/vendor reviews of your current specs — set up a "specification correlation" program.
4. See "design errors."

Figure 5.10   Document Control Errors

document control errors are large work-in-process reject rates or customer return losses which are easily tracked to documentation errors (Figure 5.10).

Documentation errors could come from many sources. Engineering change-orders are occasionally delayed due to bottlenecks or because they were misplaced in a salesperson's briefcase. Often, sales personnel do not adequately involve engineering, quality, or manufacturing personnel with the customer so that these organizational members understand the customer's requirements. Often this is also true between purchasing, vendors, and other departments within the organization. Draftspersons occasionally miss a dimension or place a dimension in the wrong location. Engineers who are supposed to check drawings before signing the signature block often do not like to act like inspectors, thus mistakes are unknowingly approved.

Another common cause for document control errors is a lack of requirements and training. Few companies develop basic drawing requirements, choosing to leave drawing consistency and integrity up to individual engineers. With engineers hired from different companies and being educated at different schools, it is highly unlikely that they all agree to the same methods for making, documenting, and upgrading drawings.

The costs associated with documentation errors can be collected from several sources. Any hours spent looking for and correcting errors should be accounted for, multiplied by a standard per hour cost for each occupational type (e.g., engineers versus draftpersons), accumulated, and plotted on a cost control chart. Additional costs which should be looked for and included in an overall cost figure include rework and scrap costs due to documentation errors and customer return costs (freight, rework, rescreening, re-inspection, retest, reshipment).

It is a relatively easy task to set up and collect such data. For example, suppose a customer returns a shipment due to the fact that the wrong revision was built. Most companies will argue with the customer in an attempt to have the product accepted, but when the return is back at the factory, costs can be calculated. A simple log of all man-hours expended on the re-inspection, rework, etc., will provide the details required for calculations of costs using standard burdened labor rates. The freight costs, in both directions, should also be added. Figure 5.11 shows a sample cost collection form which a team could develop.

Figure 5.11 shows some of the categories a CAT or FIT can brainstorm to accumulate losses due to various types of problems.

Some types of solutions could be offered for documentation errors. Probably the most powerful preventive mechanism is a complete documentation review with either the customer or the vendor (and probably both) prior to going to manufacturing. The review team should include at least the design, manufacturing and quality engineers, and the purchasing or sales representative.

Date   Customer   P/N

1. Man-hours expended to correct documentation ×
   standard burdened hourly cost $ _____
2. Return goods cost estimates
   Freight charges
      In   _____
      Out   _____
   Receiving inspection hours × std. hourly cost   _____
   Standard burdened hourly cost   _____
   Rework hours × hourly cost   _____
   Scrap costs   _____
   Re-inspection hours × standard hourly cost   _____
   Test hours × standard hourly cost   _____
                                                        Total   _____

Figure 5.11   Sample Document Error Cost Collection Form

Design Errors

Coupled with documentation errors are design errors. The need for preventive design review was discussed in Chapter 1. A team approach to preventive design review between the customer or vendor is the most powerful weapon against such potentially huge problems. Like other documentation errors, design errors can cause catastrophic financial losses.

Symptoms of design errors are large customer or vendor returns, and huge one-time rework losses. Naturally, design errors should be separated from the usual documentation errors and should be analyzed and corrected as a distinct category (Figure 5.12).

The main reason for design errors seems to be that there was "not enough time." As the old saying goes, "There is always enough time for rework, never enough time to do it right in the first place." Sales will emphatically state the urgency of getting the product into production. Purchasing will respond by ordering parts which are similar to those required. Only through teamwork and dedication can the apparent conflicts between speed and quality be neutralized.

The method for collecting and presenting design-error losses is

Symptoms:
1. *Large* customer/vendor returns.
2. Huge one-time rework losses.

Cause:
"Not enough time."

Solution:
A. Track $ losses due to design errors (yearly average).
B. Implement multidiscipline design reviews *before* production begins.
C. Involve customer/vendor in review up front.
D. Report $ changes against plan.

Figure 5.12   Design Errors (Customer and Vendor)

almost identical to other documentation cost issues. There will be freight, rework, re-inspection, scrap, retooling, recleaning, and other charges which will hit the company a few times each year. The best type of chart for displaying dollar losses due to design errors is an annualized bar chart. Simply put, the costs and losses are added up for the year (perhaps using forms similar to that in Figure 5.11) with a single vertical bar showing the amount lost, spent, or otherwise subtracted from the organization's profit.

The target for design-loss reduction usually falls within the jurisdiction of a corrective action team. The CAT needs to monitor customer complaints to determine which returns are due to design errors and separate them from other problems. Generally, multidisciplinary design reviews must be implemented before production begins. Some organizations will compromise this approach and allow prototype production without design reviews, but will require full package design reviews prior to full production. The elimination of prototype design reviews is almost always proposed for purposes of expediency (hurry!). The elimination of prototype design reviews almost always results in product failure at the customer who in turn rewards the contract for production quantities to a competitor with a better approach to business.

Symptoms:
1. Past-due printouts.
2. Frequent "emergency" reschedule (pull-ins/push-outs).
3. Frequent "expedite!!! — hot!!!" emergencies.

Causes:
1. Hockey Stick Planning: Unrealistic production schedules — unrealistic promises.

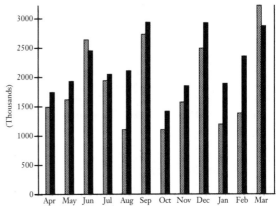

2. Quality Failures.
3. Material shortages.

Solutions:
1. JIT-IT-PULL system.
2. Eliminate overbooking to relieve capacity limitations.

TRY HONESTY

3. A. Track $ value of late deliveries (control chart).
   B. Pareto reasons for late deliveries.
   C. Use Ishikawa diagrams to look at possible causes.
   D. Take preventive action based on $ payback (inventory losses, etc.).

Figure 5.13   On-Time Customer Deliveries

On-Time Customer Deliveries

Customer deliveries can be late for any number of reasons. Most companies look at past-due reports that indicate which shipments are late. Companies that experience frequent reschedules, either delaying product or shipping it earlier than scheduled, are sure to have problems delivering shipments on time.

Taking a look at the hockey stick planning problem presented in Chapter 4 shows that sales personnel tend to make unrealistic promises to customers. Unfortunately, these promises are placed in a sales forecast which in turn is used to schedule materials and production. The hockey stick results, leaving a jerky build schedule (Figure 5.13). Overproduction occurs at the end of each quarter which leaves the first week of the next quarter without materials. No materials means no work. Employees sit around waiting for the next big bulge to come through the snake. When the bulge comes, overtime results. Overtime and the general catch-up rush means tired operators. Tired operators mean quality problems with the resultant delays or shipments which do not meet the customer's specifications.

Many organizations get into hockey stick planning by over-booking during a surge in a rapidly growing market. This is most common in the electronics industry. Sales personnel frequently commit to quantities and delivery schedules when the capacity does not exist to meet the anticipated demand. If overbooking occurs, sooner or later a shipment (probably many) will begin to become highly visible because it is late. Someone will react by moving the build schedule around to accommodate the customer, thereby upsetting applecarts of customers as the effect of schedule juggling ripples through the company. This is fire fighting, fly-by-night scheduling at its best. Many long hours are spent by managers rescheduling reschedules which were previously rescheduled. The result is chaos.

Obviously, quality problems that crop up, can and do cause customer delivery delays. Quality issues that result in delayed shipments, rework, and scrap costs should be included in the cost analysis.

From a cost perspective, two additional bits of manufacturing data are important. First, the overtime costs. If 10 percent overtime is worked and overtime is paid at time-and-a-half, it is not difficult to estimate the costs based, again, on a standard burdened labor rate. Secondly, the time operators spend sitting around doing nothing is downtime due to material shortages. Both overtime and downtime costs should be collected and plotted as targets for team improvement.

TRAINING OUTLINE

An organization interested in focusing CAT and FIT efforts on cost reduction must expect that some training must be completed. The ideas outlined in this chapter can be used to introduce team members to immediately usable techniques. Table 5.2 is a sample of a training outline that might be used for team training.

Table 5.2   Cost Analysis Techniques

1. A TQC/JIT perspective on cost analysis.
2. Definitions

    Operating Impact
    - A. Prevention costs.
    - B. Internal failure costs.
    - C. Appraisal costs.
    - D. External failure costs.

    Cost of Ownership
    - A. Between companies.
    - B. Between departments.
    - C. Between individuals.

(Table 5.2 continued)

3. Manufacturing cost concepts: rework and scrap as costs above target.

4. Examples of nonmanufacturing cost issues.

5. Team use of cost estimates.

6. Reporting.

Chapter 5 is not a particularly strong exposé of what many managers would consider real cost issues. Its intent is to arm team members with some assurances that they can keep an eye on and have some impact on costs that can save the company money. The argument is not whether the teams perform cost analyses that will pass the annual auditor's inspection, but whether team members can grasp some idea in manufacturing and nonmanufacturing circles which will help them obtain some (even crude) measure of costs, set priorities, and take corrective action to improve the situation.

Training designed to increase the current lack of knowledge is critical. Certainly, as teams develop their own measurement methods, they will be able to improve on what is currently presented.

SUMMARY

Chapter 5 attempted to show how teams in manufacturing and non-manufacturing organizational functions with knowledge of basic cost categories, can begin to perceive, measure, and reduce excessive costs due to time and quality issues. The tools used to solve problems that are measured in terms of costs are exactly the same as the tools used to solve classical quality and just-in-time problems.

The logic of team implementation and corrective action strategies and tools presented in Chapter 3 is retained when the variable changes from a count of defects or a count of hours to a count of dollars.

The basic reason for all improvement programs is to help the company become profitable. Only through profitability will the organization continue to function, thereby providing team players with a satisfactory method to earn a living.

As in other areas of expertise, team players can hardly be expected to "reduce costs" without some idea of how to reduce costs aside from removing people from the payroll. Cost-reduction programs should be part of an ongoing improvement effort, not only initiated when market demand or prices drop. The ability to identify, measure, and correct costs is not an innate ability. Training is required.

In order to assist the organization to save money, team members do not have to know and execute sophisticated accounting principles. They do, however, have to have some idea where costs are, how to perceive them, how to crudely capture them, and how to reduce them through corrective and preventive action.

6

Controlled Corporate Restructure

   All organizations are dynamic and undergoing constant change. If not identified and managed, these changes become random and reduce the organization's effectiveness. In order to control these seemingly random changes, an organized team effort must be made to sanction, focus, and direct such changes.

   It is possible to control changing corporate cultures. In order to change an organization's way of thinking and acting, deliberately led planning and corrective action must take place. A structure team approach designed to control the change must be developed and imposed. Even an organization with 100 people will appear to resist change. Larger organizations tend to take longer to change than small ones, due primarily to the momentum created by mass.

   To a great extent, the acceptance of a new structure or any other proposed change is a matter of how much commitment the organization's management demonstrates. Successful permanent TQC/JIT system implementation depends more on the desire of managers to willingly accept and implement the changes than any other single factor. Managers who knowingly ship rejectable product or verbally or covertly undermine system or team efforts can and do successfully destroy TQC/JIT efforts.

The second greatest factor required for implementation is the use of acknowledgment and reward for successful team and individual efforts. Nonsupporters should receive no rewards; supporters should be made leaders and should reap the rewards they deserve for doing an exemplary job.

The team TQC/JIT approach presented in this book is an attempt to steer and guide organizational change in a humanly positive and organizationally profitable manner.

The nature of the organization is not essential. The concepts and team structures presented are applicable to service-oriented administrative, as well as production-oriented, manufacturing functions. The perception that TQC/JIT implementation applies only to manufacturing is old fashioned and completely false. Companies choosing to implement only in manufacturing areas are missing the biggest improvement opportunities. Engineering, financial, purchasing, sales, test, research, design, inspection, documentation groups, and any other departments in a company, are primary creators of costly manufacturing problems. From a preventive point of view, problems can be eliminated only if the actual upstream causes are identified and eradicated. Invariably this means working on issues with administrative groups.

The structure proposed in this text consists primarily of three types of teams which work independently and together to bring about the desired cost effective change. In this case, a top-level team is given the responsibility for planning, nurturing, controlling, and managing TQC/JIT implementation. There is nothing new or threatening about this approach. Most organizations are managed from the top down; not enough organizations are capable of extracting and using the incredible amount of brain power which exists below the managerial levels.

It was proposed that the top-level team (TLT) be organized to include persons from the top of the organization's structure as well as a sprinkling of nonmanagerial people. This suggestion was made to ensure that the team ended up with a balance and insight not available in a team consisting only of top management. Since the TLT is responsible for planning and managing the implementation of the TQC/JIT system, and since implementation will penetrate all levels of the organization, some managerial perspective is essential.

The greatest inhibitor to the success of the TLT plan is managerial reluctance to delegate authority and responsibility throughout all organizational levels. However, with proper TQC/JIT training and direction, all organizational members will more or less understand their roles in a similar manner. There will certainly be a greater similarity of thought and action as a result of the TQC/JIT system than there probably existed prior to implementation.

With implementation, the increasing cohesiveness of the organization ensures that all members will go in the same direction, using the same tools, and will be focused on achieving the same ends: cost savings through defect and time reductions. As long as all organizational members work toward these commonly accepted goals, using commonly accepted tools and techniques, the threat of losing control by the delegation of authority will diminish and dissipate. Management will find fewer mistakes, rather than more.

Under the direction of the TLT, corrective action teams (CATs) are established, assigned interdepartmental problems to solve and are allowed to go about attacking these problems. The usual hostilities between departments tend to disappear as CATs organize and come to grips with the assigned task. The usual finger-pointing mode of operation lessens as internal customer concepts help teams to develop clear requirements with which all groups can effectively function. Attacks are begun on the extent, causes, and solutions for problems rather than on "the other" department (commonly referred to as "they" or "them").

Functional improvement teams (FITs) are formed within each direct report function. The goal of the FIT is to come to grips with and solve problems that have historically confounded departmental efforts. In a manner similar to the CATs, the FITs pass through continuous cycles of improvement within the supportive TQC/JIT structure.

Overall, continuous corrective action must be preventive in nature. Take care to reject easily identifiable "causes." The search for the cause of the cause must be ingrained in every person's attitudes, with no one being satisfied with a nonpreventive approach.

Corrections of problems should be cost justified. Solutions that do not reduce the problem significantly enough to result in cost reductions are unacceptable. Costs should be monitored, corrections tested, and only acceptable solutions implemented as permanent fixes. Manufacturing can estimate rework and scrap costs as well as the true cost of received materials. Personal computers can be used singly or in a networked manner to capture, summarize, and analyze data on a specific or general level for competent useful cost reporting. Nonmanufacturing functions can use standard burdened labor costs to prioritize and monitor estimated costs as successive waves of corrective action efforts are implemented. The strategies proposed herein do not require the expertise or manpower usually available from an accounting and financial group. Instead, nonaccountant organizational personnel are encouraged to collectively and individually develop cost estimating strategies with which to manage their own costs. Most importantly, the requirement for providing basic cost estimating training for nonaccounting persons throughout the organization has been recognized. It simply is not realistic to expect people to cut costs when they have no way to estimate the best costs to cut which will improve rather than reduce functional capabilities.

Special teams are formed to effectively implement many of the requirements imposed by preparation for just-in-time strategies. These special teams are responsible for studying a large variety of JIT requirements and activities and finding ways to support the overall system by constantly improving the system. Often, a pilot line can be established for other special team experimentation and improvement. Statistical process control can be used in conjunction with the changes to determine the level of success. KANBAN pull systems are set up to force line balance and material flow to managerial levels. Reviews of designs are accomplished with the intent of improving the company's ability to manufacture the product in the simplest, cheapest manner with the least number of parts. Preventive maintenance teams are charged with the responsibility of making sure that tooling, fixtures, and equipment are always capable of performing the job for which they were designed. The vendor relationship team focuses on qualifying the best available vendors and working with these vendors to establish and maintain a long-term relationship beneficial to both companies. Piece-parts and tooling are looked at to determine ways to foolproof assembly and machining. Competent and professional training is established in order to support the ever-growing requirements for controlled change. Futuristic tooling and process improvement investigations are launched and maintained to prevent the technology from lagging behind competition and in an effort to continuously solve problems in a cost-effective manner.

These and many other special focus teams constantly and relentlessly work to improve the service and manufacturing processes upon which the organization depends.

Appendices

APPENDIX A.1
Model Top-Level Team Plan

Statement of problem: Dedication to TQC

Name of team	Top-level team												
Leader/members	All				Total quality system								
					Implementation action items and corrective action planning								
Activity	Person Respons	Feb 1 2 3 4	March 1 2 3 4	April 1 2 3 4	May 1 2 3 4	June 1 2 3 4	July 1 2 3 4	Aug 1 2 3 4	Sept 1 2 3 4	Status
Measure quality attitudes	MH	X								
Report to TLT	MH	X								
Set improvement priorities	TLT		X							
Form FITs in functions	TLT		X——Ongoing							
Review status of TLT plan	TLT		X——————Ongoing							
Write and distribute companywide policy	TLT			X						

APPENDIX A.2

Statement of problem:	Information maintenance and distribution										
Name of team	Top-level team			Total quality system							
Leader/members	JG			Implementation action items and corrective action planning							
Activity	Person Respons	Feb 1 2 3 4	March 1 2 3 4	April 1 2 3 4	May 1 2 3 4	June 1 2 3 4	July 1 2 3 4	Aug 1 2 3 4	Sept 1 2 3 4	Status
Set up employee orientation program	JG	X—X								
Orient all employees	JG	X—X								
Determine and provide in-depth training	JG		X————————————————X							
Communicate activities through newsletter			X—Ongoing—							
Notify customers and vendors through visits				X—X						

APPENDIX A.3

Statement of problem:	Personnel responsibilities and accountability									
Name of team	Top-level team			Total quality system						
Leader/members	JS			Implementation action items and corrective action planning						
Activity	Person Respons	Feb 1 2 3 4	March 1 2 3 4	April 1 2 3 4	May 1 2 3 4	June 1 2 3 4	July 1 2 3 4	Aug 1 2 3 4	Sept 1 2 3 4	Status
Write and approve policy	TLT		X							
Develop individual objective forms	JS		X							
Train all managers to use forms	JS			X—X						
Implement ACC/RES system	TLT Staff				X ———————— Ongoing					

APPENDIX A.4

Statement of problem: Showing appreciation for accomplishments										
Name of team	Top-level team					Total quality system				
Leader/members	JSG					Implementation action items and corrective action plan				
Activity	Person Respons	Feb 1 2 3 4	March 1 2 3 4	April 1 2 3 4	May 1 2 3 4	June 1 2 3 4	July 1 2 3 4	Aug 1 2 3 4	Sept 1 2 3 4	Status
Define award criteria for individuals and teams	JSG		X							
Develop levels of awards	JSG		X							
Inform all personnel	JSG		X							
Implement award system	TLT			X——Ongoing—						
TLT monitors and issues high-level awards publicly	TLT			X——Ongoing—						

APPENDIX A.5

Statement of problem: Sharing of results										
Name of team	Top-level team			Total quality system						
Leader/members	DR			Implementation action items and corrective action planning						
Activity	Person Respons	Feb 1 2 3 4	March 1 2 3 4	April 1 2 3 4	May 1 2 3 4	June 1 2 3 4	July 1 2 3 4	Aug 1 2 3 4	Sept 1 2 3 4	Status
Determine methods to measure quality costs	DR			X						
Incorporate quality cost measures into training	DR			X						
Work with teams to set quality cost reduction targets	TLT			X————		Ongoing—				
Develop and communicate corporate level goals	TLT		X							
Provide continuous cost tracking assistance and review	DR/ TLT				X—Ongoing—					
Establish and implement companywide reporting	DR			X						
Report results in conjunction with reward system						X— Ongoing—				
Provide methods for formal TLT review				X						

APPENDIX A.6

Statement of problem: Perpetuate motivational levels										
Name of team	Top-level team				Total quality system					
Leader/members	JR				Implementation action items and corrective action planning					
Activity	Person Respons	Feb 1 2 3 4	March 1 2 3 4	April 1 2 3 4	May 1 2 3 4	June 1 2 3 4	July 1 2 3 4	Aug 1 2 3 4	Sept 1 2 3 4	Status
Establish newsletter to publish success	JR		X			X			X	Newsletter will be quarterly
Set up semi-annual recognition dinner/day	JR					X				
Provide budget for award structure	TLT			X						
Establish manager measures for team leadership	TLT				X					
Establish employee poster system	JR			X						
Provide TLT review summary of motivational efforts	JR		X			X			X	

APPENDIX A.7

Statement of problem: Maintenance of FIT/CAT implementation activities										
Name of team:	Top-level team				Total quality system					
Leader/members:	RBM				Implementation action items and corrective action planning					
Activity	Person Respons	Feb 1 2 3 4	March 1 2 3 4	April 1 2 3 4	May 1 2 3 4	June 1 2 3 4	July 1 2 3 4	Aug 1 2 3 4	Sept 1 2 3 4	Status
All TLT members to attend FIT/CAT meetings	TLT		X—Ongoing							
Establish review system for TLT meeting attendance	RBM		X—X							
Set up tracking system for team progress	RBM			X						
Track training of all old and new employees/report	RBM		X—Ongoing							
Establish corrective action teams and monitor	TLT		X—Ongoing							
Review overall TLT plan status			X			X			X	During quarterly review

APPENDIX B
Sample GANTT Planning Chart

Statement of problem:

Name of FIT/CAT

Leader/members

Total quality system

Implementation action items and corrective action planning

Activity	Person Respons	Feb 1 2 3 4	March 1 2 3 4	April 1 2 3 4	May 1 2 3 4	June 1 2 3 4	July 1 2 3 4	Aug 1 2 3 4	Sept 1 2 3 4	Status

APPENDIX C.1
Model Accountability Forms
Corrective Action Team Contract

Page _____ of _____
Date _____

CAT Name: Leader: Start Date:

Objective of CAT:

Signatures of Approval (members)

No.	Action Item	Resp	Start Plan/Act	Due Plan/Act
1				
2				
3				
4				
5				
6				
7				
8				
9				

APPENDIX C.2
Individual Objectives Contract

Page _____ of _____

Date _____

Employee Name: Title: Dept.:

Objectives	Target Points	Target Completion			
		Q1	Q2	Q3	Q4

Record of variances between target and actual completion:

Total points available = 100

Total points earned = _____

Comments/reschedules/barriers

Signatures:

Supervisor _____ Employee _____

Date of next review _____

APPENDIX D
Model Meeting Agenda/Minutes Form
Team Meeting Agenda/Minutes

FIT/CAT Name _____   Date: _____

Attendees _____   _____   _____

           _____   _____   _____

           _____   _____   _____

           _____   _____   _____

Agenda Item	Discussion Leader	Time/Item
1		
2		
3		
4		

Minutes/Action Items	Responsibility	Date

Next Meeting:
Date: _____ Time: _____ Location: _____

Agenda Item	Discussion Leader	Time/Item

APPENDIX E
Procurement Quality Procedures

I. Purpose – The purpose of this procedure is to establish standards for vendor qualification and certification.

II. Scope – The procedure covers basic quality related requirements for (the company's) vendors, purchasing, procurement quality, and engineering as they relate to the qualification and certification of direct material vendors. Each separate part number purchased from each separate vendor is covered by this procedure. If a vendor is certified on one part number, a new part number which is to be evaluated will go through the same procedure for qualification and certification. Vendors will be notified of the minimum quantities and minimum order period required for certification.

III. Procedure

A. Vendor Qualification Program

1. Purchasing proposals

The purchasing department shall propose that vendors be reviewed for qualification. Purchasing shall provide the procurement quality group with a review package which consists of the following:

a. A drawing or set of drawings for all parts proposed for purchase.

b. A notice of the scheduled review date complete with the vendor's address, phone number, quality manager's name, and any other pertinent information which will help with the review.

c. In the case of "generic" parts, the parts will be delivered with items a. and b. to the procurement quality engineer for review and first-article inspection/test.

2. Vendor site review

A vendor site review team consisting of representatives from purchasing, quality, and engineering shall visit the vendor's manufacturing site and review the vendor's quality, delivery, manufacturing process capabilities, using the attached review form. The team must unanimously approve the vendor, as indicated by approval signatures, prior to the awarding of a "first article" order.

The main quality objectives of the site review shall be to determine the vendor's capability and commitment to prevent quality problems from occurring through the use or implementation of a preventive quality system.

3. Design review

A design review team consisting of representatives from purchasing, quality, and engineering shall meet with the vendor's representatives prior to the building or submission of first article parts. The groups shall review the design and agree on all dimensions.

All drawings will show critical parameters per specification. No critical parameters will be negotiable at design review.

Data requirements for first article, ongoing correlation samples, and process control charts will be determined during the design review. It is the vendor's responsibility to supply these data with shipments.

NOTE: No sales orders will be issued until the proposed vendor has been qualified by the site and design reviews.

4. First article qualification

The vendor will submit first article samples and measurement data on quantities determined during the design review. Procurement quality personnel will inspect/test first article parts per appropriate quality specifications and drawings. Data will be compared to the vendor's data to determine whether or not first-article correlation has been established.

A report will be written by the procurement quality group which will clearly reflect any discrepancies in the customer data and first-article parts. The report will note the disposition of the parts and highlight required corrective action for the vendor's production or measurement methods.

Appropriate correlation coefficients, bivariate frequency distributions, and dependent t-tests will be performed between customer and vendor measurements on each variable. These analyses and the conclusions drawn will be noted in the report.

5. Measurement/test correlation

The vendor shall supply measurement/test correlation samples and data every fourth shipment after production orders have been released. The size of these samples will be determined at design review time. Each piece in the sample will be clearly labeled to identify it in relation to the data supplied by the vendor. Procurement quality personnel will report on the correlation between measurements. This report will follow the following format:

MEASUREMENT/TEST CORRELATION REPORT

REPORT DATE_____   VENDOR NAME_____

DATE PARTS RECEIVED _____ VENDOR PART NUMBER _____ REV_____

INSPECTOR_____   ENGINEER_____

COMPANY PART NUMBER _____ REV_____ DESCRIPTION_____

Statement of measurement:

Procedures used:

Data analysis:
(Attach additional sheets if necessary)

Conclusions:

6. Source inspection
   In the event that a qualified vendor is experiencing difficulty in either measurement or production, procurement quality personnel will source inspect the vendor's product prior to shipment.

7. Bill-back for failed lots
   The vendor will be billed for the fully burdened cost of screening lots which fail any audit and which must be screened by company personnel.

8. Lot control
   Vendors will clearly mark the smallest of each packing container with lot control numbers. The number will be identified with the prefix "LOT #." This number should provide traceability to a particular manufacturing run and also to the lot of material used by the vendor to manufacture the lot.

   The lot number will also appear on the vendor's packing slip. For instances where more than one lot is shipped at one time, corresponding lot numbers will appear on the packing slip. Receiving inspection personnel will take evaluation samples from each separate lot.

B. Vendor certification
   The goal of the vendor certification program is to eliminate receiving inspection. This can best be accomplished when vendors are placed on a dock-to-stock program. All qualified vendors will be required to fulfill the following requirements:

1. Statistical process control requirements
   Vendors shall provide receiving inspection with statistical process control charts and process capability data with each shipment. One control chart will be required for each critical parameter shown on the drawing for the piece part as indicated in Paragraph III A 3.

   Control charts shall show the part number, date of samples, process average, range, upper and lower control limits, dimensional nominal and tolerance limits. Any out-of-control conditions will be noted on the chart along with corrective actions taken.

These charts will be evaluated by procurements using standard control chart interpretation methods.

Quality procurement will assist the vendor in the establishment of an appropriate statistical process control system.

2. Measurement/test correlation samples

Receiving inspection shall measure critical parameters on samples supplied per Paragraph III A 5.

Comparison of matched variables shall be accomplished using bivariate frequency distributions, correlation coefficients, and dependent t-tests, or through other appropriate procedures.

3. Skip-lot procedures

Once the vendor has demonstrated that the process is in control using control charts and that correlation has been established according to Paragraphs III B2 and 3, the vendor will be placed on skip-lot inspection per standards.

4. Dock-to-stock status

A vendor successfully completing eight weeks of skip-lot inspection with no lot failures will be evaluated for dock-to-stock status.

Considering the following formula to evaluate material costs, vendors will be placed on dock-to-stock status when:

$$P < k1/k2$$

where

P is the average fraction defective in incoming lots of parts, $k1$ is the cost to inspect one part at receiving inspection, and $k2$ is the cost to completely rework, re-inspect, and retest an assembly that fails because a defective part was put into the production line

When $P > k1/k2$, 100 percent inspection of the incoming materials will be required with the costs paid by the vendor.

APPENDIX F
Model Vendor Qualification Survey

1. Quality planning questions
   - Does the vendor have a written quality plan?
   - Does the quality plan include other departments in the company?
   - Does a status report exist which shows the status of plan implementation?
   - Is there hard (directly observable) evidence to indicate that the plan is being implemented?
   - Are ongoing quality planning functions in existence to address new requirements?

2. Quality policy questions
   - Does the company have a written quality policy?
   - Is the policy posted where personnel can read it?
   - Is the policy signed by officers of the company?
   - Does evidence exist to indicate that personnel understand and believe in the policy?

3. Management teamwork questions
   - Does an interdepartmental management team exist to oversee the quality function?
   - Which departments are involved in the management team?

4. Design reviews
   - Does the vendor have a design review procedure?
   - Will the vendor agree to review company designs with the customer prior to production purchase order approval?
   - Which vendor departments will be represented during the design review?

5. Employee training program questions
   - Are new employees given formal operation training prior to going on the production line?
   - Are employees given upgrade or cross training?
   - Are employees trained in quality procedures and specifications pertinent to their operations?
   - Are employees trained in TQC and JIT techniques?

6. Data system questions
   - Does the vendor employ statistical process control charts?
   - Are mechanisms in place to ensure that the data are used to manage/control quality from a 100 percent employee involvement/team approach?
   - Is the vendor capable of providing control charts from final and in-process quality audit stations?
   - Are employees trained and implementing in-process SPC?
   - Is there evidence on control charts to indicate that out-of-control problems are quickly identified and corrected?

- Do reviewers of control charts discriminate between system causes and special causes?
- Does the vendor have a cost analysis system in place which highlights high loss processes and procedures?

7. Preventive action questions
   - Is there evidence to indicate that preventive maintenance of tooling/fixtures is carried out?
   - Do test and inspection equipment have up-to-date calibration stickers?
   - Do managers meet to assign action items on system-caused defects?
   - Do operators, engineers, etc., meet as FIT or CAT teams to eliminate special and system causes?
   - Is there evidence to indicate that a preventive attitude is taken during corrective actions?

8. Organizational questions
   - Does the vendor have top-level, FIT, and CAT teams organized and operational to guide an intensive quality effort?
   - Is the quality organization centralized or integrated throughout the company?
   - To whom does the top-level quality manager report?

9. Vendor liaison questions
   - Are the vendor's vendors reviewed for their abilities to prevent quality problems?

10. Customer interface questions
    - Is there a specific vendor representative assigned to handle problems with the customer?
    - Is there an ongoing vendor-customer correlation program in place?
    - Are lot numbers provided on each of the smallest shipping containers?
    - Does the vendor have the capability to provide 100 percent inspection of lots which fail either the customer's or vendor's final quality audit?

References

1. Author unknown. "How to Read a Financial Report," Fourth Edition, Merrill Lynch, Pierce, Fenner & Smith, Inc., republished as "The Keys to Financial Ease," *Quality*, pp. 28 – 34, November 1982.

2. Campenella, Jack, Chairman, Quality Costs Committee. *Guide for Reducing Quality Costs*, 2nd Ed., American Society for Quality Control, Milwaukee, 1987.

3. Drucker, Peter F. *Management: Tasks, Responsibilities, Practices*, Harper and Row, 1974.

4. Feigenbaum, A. V. *Total Quality Control: Engineering and Management*, McGraw-Hill, New York, 1961.

5. Ferguson, George A. *Statistical Analysis in Psychology and Education*, McGraw-Hill, New York, 1976.

6. Hagan, John T., Ed. ASQC Quality Costs Committee, *Principles of Quality Costs*, American Society for Quality Control, Milwaukee, 1986.

7. Herskovits, Melville J. *Cultural Dynamics*, Alfred A. Knopf, New York, 1967.

8. Hutchens, Spencer. "What Customers Want: Results of ASQC/Gallup Survey," *Qual. Prog.*, American Society for Quality Control, Milwaukee, February 1989.

9. Ishikawa, Kaoru. *Guide to Quality Control*, Asian Productivity Organization, Tokyo, Japan, 1982.

10. Juran, J. M., Ed. *Quality Control Handbook*, McGraw-Hill, 1974.

11. Ott, Ellis R. *Process Quality Control: Troubleshooting and Interpretation of Data*, McGraw-Hill, 1975.

12. Peters, Tom. *Thriving On Chaos: Handbook for a Management Revolution*, Alfred A. Knopf, New York, 1988.

13. Peters, Tom and Robert H. Watterman. *In Search of Excellence*, Random House, New York, 1983.

14. Pittiglio, Rabin, Todd and McGrath. "1985 Inventory Performance in the Electronics Industry," *Man. Stud. No. 9*, Palo Alto, California, 1985.

15. Ryan, John M. "Some Perspectives on the Collection and Analysis of Quality Data," *QualTest-2 Conf. Proceed.* (pp. 26-9 through 26-16), American Society for Nondestructive Testing, Inc., American Society for Quality Control, and Society of Manufacturing Engineers, Dallas, 1983.

16. Ryan, John M. "The Impact of Statistical Quality Control on Feedback, Teamwork, and Motivation," *QualTest-2 Conf. Proceed.* (pp. 29-21 through 29-26), American Society for Nondestructive Testing, Inc., American Society for Quality Control, Society of Manufacturing Engineers, Dallas, 1983.

17. Ryan, John M. and H. Wong. "Breaking Down the Barriers," *Quality* (pp. 40 – 42), Hitchock Publishing Company, Wheaton, IL, April 1984.

18. Ryan, John M. and A. Rafiq. "A High-Tech Sight for Cost Targets," *ASQC 41st Annual Quality Congress Transactions* (pp. 382 – 388), American Society for Quality Control, Minneapolis, 1987.

19. Ryan, John M. and H. Wong. "Tiered Data Systems for Statistical Quality Control," *Quality Progress* (pp. 22 – 24), American Society for Quality Control, Milwaukee, September 1984.

20. Snee, Ronald D., L. B. Hare and J. R. Trout. *Experiments in Industry: Design, Analysis, and Interpretation of Results*, American Society for Quality Control, Milwaukee, 1985.

21. Storm, David J. "The Way to World-Class: Eliminate NVA," *Just-in-Time/Qual. Conf. Proceed.* (pp. 52 – 54), American Production & Inventory Control Society, Atlanta, GA, 1987.

22. Wick, Charles and Raymond F. Veilleux Eds. *Tool and Manufacturing Engineers Handbook: Volume 4, Quality Control and Assembly*, Society of Manufacturing Engineers, Dearborn, MI, 1987.

23. Winchell, William O., Ed. ASQC Quality Costs Committee. *Guide for Managing Supplier Quality Costs*, American Society for Quality Control, Milwaukee, 1987.

24. Webster, Merriam A. *Webster's New World Dictionary of the American Language*, G. & C. Merriam Company, Springfield, MA, 1981.

25. Deming, W. Edwards. *Quality, Productivity and Competitive Position*, Massachusetts Institute for Technology, Center for Advanced Engineering Study, 1982.

Index